Summary Bundle: Science | Readtrepreneur Publishing: Includes Summary of Collusion & Summary of Cosmos

ABBEY BEATHAN

Legal & Disclaimer

Legal & Disclaimer

The information contained in this book is not designed to replace or take the place of any form of medicine or professional medical advice. The information in this book has been provided for educational and entertainment purposes only.

The information contained in this book has been compiled from sources deemed reliable, and it is accurate to the best of the Author's knowledge; however, the Author cannot guarantee its accuracy and validity and cannot be held liable for any errors or omissions. Changes are periodically made to this book. You must consult your doctor or get professional medical advice before using any of the suggested remedies, techniques, or information in this book. Images used in this book are not the same as of those of the actual book. This is a totally separate and different entity from that of the original book titled: "Collusion"

Upon using the information contained in this book, you agree to hold harmless the Author from and against any damages, costs, and expenses, including any legal fees potentially resulting from the application of any of the information provided by this guide. This disclaimer applies to any damages or injury caused by the use and application, whether directly or indirectly, of any advice or information presented, whether for breach of contract, tort, negligence, personal injury, criminal intent, or under any other cause of action.

You agree to accept all risks of using the information presented inside this book. You need to consult a professional medical practitioner in order to ensure you are both able and healthy enough to participate in this program.

Table of Contents

The Book at a Glance

This book was authored by Luke Harding, a writer for the Guardian. He has been designated as the Russian expert in the said news outlet.

The book tackles the things that transpired before, during, and after the most recent United States presidential election in 2016. Most of the information written here is readily available from news archives. You can say that this is a compilation of news that is connected to the Russia and Trump collusion.

Another thing to note is that this book primarily focuses on the Russian aspect of the story and the Steele dossier. If you are expecting detailed write-ups about the movements of the "Trump team," then this book will provide you little additional knowledge.

Sources of information used to create this book are personal accounts of Luke Harding, his interviews with the prominent people included in this book, and the news. The story is written in a creative nonfiction way. Expect that it would be told as if you were reading a spy novel.

Another thing that you should remember is that Luke

Harding himself admitted that this only scratches the surface of the whole collusion investigation and allegation. According to him, it is just almost 15% of the story, including information about the collusion. The remaining 85% is still hidden, waiting to be discovered and told. The rest will be about the personalities that played major and minor roles in Russia's involvement with Trump.

The first half of the book mostly talks about and follows the story of Paul Manafort, Trump's former campaign advisor. It also discusses how the KGB, FSB, and GRU worked behind the scenes in order to gain an advantage on the United States.

The second half is a mix of additional information about Trump, the FBI, and the cash flow from Russia to Trump. This primarily involves Donald Trump Jr., Paul Manafort, and Jared Kushner. Aside from them, certain oligarchs, minigarchs, and key figures in Russian politics are highlighted.

It is also important that you familiarize yourself with Christopher Steele's memos or the infamous dossier. It is referred in the book multiple times, and it is best that you get to know more about it for a better reading experience.

Overall, the book is a nice source of information for people who have not been tuned in to the news lately and want to know more how Russian intelligence agencies, particularly the FSB, KGB, and GRU, operate.

On the other hand, this will give you an inkling on dirty politics and the intelligence industry. Together with that, Luke Harding paints a lovely picture of Moscow in the book. It is as if you were actually where the events happened.

Anyway, without further ado, here is a quick review and summarization of Collusion: Secret Meetings, Dirty Money, and How Russia Helped Donald Trump Win.

Prologue: Meeting

The book starts in Orbis Business Intelligence. This is where Christopher Steele, the writer of the Trump-Russia dossier, has worked ever since he quit being a spy for the United Kingdom.

In the spying business, you never run out of work. There is always something to learn. And the demand for information is always at an all-time high, especially now that the world is in the digital age.

The definition and methods of war have changed. You do not need guns and bullets to topple a man or a government. All you need now are a computer, diligence, time, and the key people to talk to.

Now, America is faced with one of the biggest and most scandalous issues yet: the collusion between the most powerful man in the United States and its rival, Russia.

Steele was one of the biggest players in this business. And Luke Harding got the chance to get him to talk — even if his lips were still tightly sealed.

Chapter 1: The End of History Not

This chapter focuses on how the KGB was powerful back in the 1990s. They could do whatever they wanted. Even if the relations between the Western countries and the Soviet Union have warmed up, the KGB was still working furtively behind the scenes.

The KGB kept watch of Western diplomats, particularly the one in the UK embassy. Christopher Steele, the diplomat, was an intelligence officer employed by SIS or the Secret Intelligence Service. He is a Cambridge (a school where MI6 mostly get their people from) graduate, and was in MI6 for three years. At present, he is most known as the one who wrote the Trump-Russia dossier.

This chapter discussed a bit of his background as an SIS and MI6 agent. It is also mixed with a bit of Russian history.

Multiple events happened in the 1990s. First was the fall of the Berlin Wall. Second was the revolution of the Baltic States against the Soviet Union. Third was the rise of a democratic president in Soviet Russia. Fourth was the famine in the country.

Christopher Steel witnessed all of those events. And unlike

other diplomats in the country, he had internal access to off-limit areas in the Soviet Union like Samara and Stalin's underground bunker. And during his stay in the country, he also witnessed the coup against Gorbachev and its failure.

Despite the positive shift away from communism, groups like the KGB stand as the biggest hindrances in the progression of Soviet Russia.

But after a few years, the Soviet Union was replaced by the Russian Federation. Together with the removal of the union, the KGB was also dissolved. However, even if the KGB was removed, KGB operatives and its high-ranking officials couldn't move on. One of those people was Vladimir Putin. He considered the removal of the USSR as a huge disaster.

As a replacement for the KGB, the Federal Security Service, or FSB, was formed. It directly competed against the MI6.

Years smoothly passed by. Steele had been assigned missions around Russia, the UK, and France. He even started his own family. However, things changed in 1999: The list of MI6 operatives were leaked on the Internet. His cover was blown, together with his coworkers. This made them vulnerable and their operations limited. He couldn't go back to Russia anymore.

On the other side of the world, Putin was busy fulfilling his ambitions. He became FSB chief. Then he became prime minister. Then he became president. The assumption that Russia would embrace democracy became a fantasy. With Putin, a known loyalist of the USSR, as president, many were alarmed.

Aside from having an idea of his ideology, details of Putin's life and activities were virtually unknown. Since Putin came into power, the security against spies and other information-gathering people was strengthened.

The US envied the UK for obtaining a lot of information about Russia. And because terrorists and radical Islamic groups became major threats, the US lowered the priority of gathering intelligence about the new Russia.

Going back to Steele, his position in the MI6 improved. He was in charge of various investigations including the poisoning of Alexander Litvinenko, a defector and former officer in the FSB.

After twenty years working as an intelligence officer for the UK, he quit and started Orbis Business Intelligence Ltd., a research and intelligence firm. It seemed that he had no plan to stop gathering intelligence. The only difference now was that he wasn't being backed and funded by the government.

He teamed up with Glenn Simpson, a former journalist from the Wall Street Journal. And his stories primarily focused on Russia. He also started a small company called Fusion GPS. The business worked on analyzing events and news in Russia.

One of the first cases that Steele worked on with Simpson was the use of Putin's influence in FIFA. The investigation resulted into the arrest of seven officials in FIFA and the indictment of 14 officials in the United States. This event made Steele's reputation soar.

His work on Russia had extended to Ukraine. However, his work was turned around when Donald Trump started to gain traction in the presidential election. The Washington Free Beacon hired Fusion to do some background research on Trump. Note that the Beacon is backed by wealthy investors that are allied with Trump's opponents.

Steele started with Paul Manafort, Trump's campaign manager at that time. Since he was obsessed and specialized with Russia, his first move was to check if Trump was connected to them. After some time digging for information, he struck gold. He found a connection between the Kremlin and Trump.

According to him, Russian intelligence has been rearing Trump for half a decade. The move was endorsed by Putin.

This "cultivation" allowed Trump to get better business in Russia. FSB also gained materials that could allow them to blackmail Trump. And the FSB collected dirt against Hillary to be used later.

This started the whole collusion thing. And the dossier had gotten out of the bag.

Chapter 2: I Think He's an Idiot

Victor Podobnyy was a disappointed Russian spy sent to New York as a diplomat and economic intelligence gatherer for the SVR. The FBI monitored him and discovered that SVR spies like Podobnyy were not happy with their jobs.

In 2010, the cover of 10 SVR agents in the United States was blown. Most of them were spies, not diplomats. They were considered "illegals" and were immediately dealt with. Since Podobnyy was a diplomat, he was spared but was still continuously being tracked and monitored.

Podobnyy continued with his mission. And along the way, he was tasked to get more spies or sources of information. He had a hard time acquiring Americans who were willing to work with him. However, he found one in the form of an energy consultant. He was Carter Page. The same Page who will be one of Trump's foreign policy advisers.

Carter Page was difficult to deal with according to Podobnyy. As his "American intelligence source," Carter spent more time in Russia than Podobnyy. He is also known as a Russian sympathizer and was often found to be siding with Putin instead of President Barack Obama.

The funny thing was that he was not all for Trump in the beginning. But at the start of the presidential election, people found him together with Trump. Speculations said that Trump must have picked Page just because he loathed Clinton and Obama.

Page has been found to be flying over to Moscow several times during the Trump campaign phase. He delivered speeches that were supposed to be about energy, but was mired in the topic of the United States' attempt to spread democracy in the world. According to people who attended, it was a weird speech.

On the other hand, according to the dossier, Page was not in Russia just to deliver some strange speech. He was there to meet with a former Russian spy, Igor Sechin. Sechin is a man close to Putin. He had worked with him for more than 30 years. Now, he is currently executive chairman of Rosneft's, a state-owned oil company.

Page secretly met with another man, Igor Diveykin — Putin's senior official internal political department and presidential administration.

The meeting with Sechin was all about lifting the sanctions that the Obama administration applied to Rosneft. And the second sanction that he wished to be lifted was the sanctions on Ukraine. In exchange, Sechin bribed Page with 19% of Rosneft's brokerage.

The meeting with Diveykin, on the other hand, was all about threatening and blackmailing. The meeting revealed that Russia had information that could put Trump down and ruin his goal, which was to become the next POTUS. Carter Page has denied all of these events taking place.

As Carter Page's constant communications with Russian spies continued, the FBI took notice of him. There were attempts to bug him, but it was difficult. When he was interviewed by an agent of counterintelligence, Gregory Monaghan, Page said that he was not doing anything wrong and then suddenly stopped communicating with Russians.

However, that did not stop the agency on pursuing his case. The FBI provided evidences to the Foreign Intelligence Surveillance Agency or FISA. The judge deemed Page as a possible Russian agent. With that, a warrant was generated for him. And his electronic communications were surveilled.

When the case with Page grew public, the Trump team immediately disavowed him. His career with Trump was over.

After Trump won the election, the things Sechin had said to Page came true. Rosneft immediately sold 19.5% of its stocks.

The buyers of the stocks are confusing. According to Rosneft, the buyers were Glencore and Intesa Sanpaolo. However, the remaining quarter of the sale has an unknown buyer — almost 4.87%.

Since the deal was over, and Page was already casted off by the Trump administration, he had nowhere to go. It could have been okay, but his problems would multiply even further after the dossier was released to the public.

Chapter 3: Published and Be Damned

The dossier had been circulating among the media for quite some time. However, it was mostly ignored or kept hidden. The dossier was not spread around by Steele. It was Simpson who wanted people to know about it. After all, Steele was mostly sending the reports to Fusion.

Then everyone made their move. Russian correspondents were into the case and allegations. The Clinton camp researched about the alleged event that involved Trump and Moscow prostitutes. And journalists continued to verify the contents of the dossier.

One of the reasons why it was not released to the public immediately was the risk that the media outlet might come out as a source of wrong information and defamation. Also, verifying the authenticity of the information in the dossier would take time and required the intervention of the authorities. So, the media needed to wait for the perfect opportunity.

Then information about the FBI taking a case into the FISA came about. It was safe to report it, and it was the perfect opening for the dossier and the rest of the scandalous information about the collusion to be disclosed to the public.

CNN was the one that made the bold move of starting the story. It published the story 10 days before Trump's inauguration. And as expected, the channel received a lot of flak. However, they did not release the full story and the contents of the dossier.

Here came BuzzFeed. A then-young publishing company that focused on publishing listicles, it was starting to enter the world of serious journalism. They had the guts to publish the contents of the dossier online — a 35-page report.

Trump reacted and used Twitter to let the public know about his response. He said that it was fake news and it was just a political witch-hunt. And those lines would be repeated again and again — even until today.

For its initial publication, the dossier's author, Steele, was unmentioned. Then multiple events that involved killing took place. First, it was the opposition journalist Anna Politkovskaya. Then, it was Litvinenko, a defector who denounced Putin. Lastly, it was Nigel Inkster, the SIS' former deputy director.

BuzzFeed did not escape the consequences of creating a huge wave and sensation over the dossier. Most media outlets, even the Washington Post, bashed the company. Other top-tier news outlets followed suit.

This event and Trump's reactions revitalized journalism. With Trump vilifying media as fake and other unpleasant adjectives, journalists felt that they were more than needed. On top of the numerous slip-ups and lies that came from Trump, they were compelled to work harder, especially when it came to fact checking.

Also, because there was a lot of information that needed to be verified, news organizations tended to cooperate to find information together instead of traditionally competing against each other. Leaks have been sought after and became abundant during the Trump presidency. But despite all those, the truth remains elusive.

Trump was not only the one persecuted because of the dossier. Putin was also under fire, and it was up to Peskov to handle the criticisms.

On the other hand, Putin did air some reactions about the trouble caused by the dossier. He defended Trump, saying that he was immune to beautiful girls, let alone prostitutes. And seemingly, during his speech on defending Trump, he jabbed a bit on Steele.

And of course, after Putin's speech, Trump immediately vented his reaction on Twitter — further reinforcing that the dossier was just a propaganda set by his opponents.

At this point, the FBI was still struggling to verify the claims in the dossier. The problem now was that Trump had started to make moves that would benefit Russia a lot. First, he took all the attention to him in international news. It effectively made the world forget that Russia was continuously grabbing land.

Second, Trump was trying to destabilize the North Atlantic Treaty Organization or NATO. NATO is basically an alliance between European countries and the United States to deter terrorism and aggressive nations. Some of the words he used to describe NATO were "unfair," "expensive," and "obsolete."

After the public and the news outlets went crazy about the dossier, Steele disappeared. According to one of his friends, it was a shame that the dossier and his face appeared in public. As an intelligence agent, Steele's work requires that his work and face remain unrevealed.

Also, he was not running for his life. He knows well how the FSB works, and they do not kill foreign spies. No assassins or hit men were after him. He just wanted to avoid the press and the limelight.

When it came to interview attempts, he did not accept any since he couldn't really answer anything. After all, his sources would be questioned. And those sources of information would be in greater danger than he would ever be.

Chapter 4: Hack

The FSB is known to be brutal against traitors. And its cyber security division is certainly good at its job. However, there is one group they have trouble dealing with: Humpty Dumpty or Shaltai-Boltai. Unlike hackers in WikiLeaks that expose secrets for public viewing, Humpty Dumpty dig information that they can use for blackmailing and extortion — not to mention they do not want to be known. They operated outside the country: specifically, in Thailand.

Before they became extortionists, they were a bit idealistic. But they realized the possible profit that could be gained in exchange for well-hidden information. They started to target high-profile personalities in the government. They are good to the point they have a well-documented file that involved every meal Putin has eaten and all the messages he has sent and received.

They were successful in their business. If the target was not profitable, the information they had would be auctioned off. And it didn't matter who bought the information. It could be from the UK or the US. As long as there is money, information would be given.

The dossier also contained information on the movement of Russia and the high-profile hackers. And it is unfortunate that Russia is unsuccessful when it comes to getting information through the Internet from world-leading countries.

During the popular DNC hacks and the election, three people were arrested and imprisoned at Lefortovo. They were Dokuchaev, Stoyanov, and Mikhailov. Dmitry Dokuchaev was a former criminal hacker for the FSB. Ruslan Stoyanov was a former Department K cybercrime unit agent. And Sergei Mikhailov was the former deputy head of FSB's Security Center.

Another suspicious death after the release of the dossier was the death of Oleg Erovinkin. He was an FSB general, and he was well-trusted in the government. He served as the link between Rosneft and the government. He held many secrets. And then he was found dead in a car on a parking lot.

Suspicions grew that he was one of Steele's intelligence sources. However, Steele has denied it. And as the FSB said, it was just a case of heart attack, and Steele has said that people just sometimes die. Despite the alleged sudden death of Erovinkin, the FSB and the Kremlin were doing some spring cleaning to clear American and British spy networks within.

Other deaths include those of Russian diplomats and a consular deputy commander named Sergei Krivov. There was no pattern with the deaths. They occurred in different locations outside and inside Russia. One probable cause was suicide because of the failure of keeping secrets.

After the election, Obama immediately acted upon the cyber-attacks. The FBI and Homeland Security identified two groups. The first one was codenamed Cozy Bear and identified as Advanced Persistent Threat 29 or APT29. The second one was codenamed Fancy Bear and identified as APT28.

The groups were able to infiltrate US government employees and political parties. They were victimized with simple phishing links. It allowed the group to gain access to the email accounts of the victims.

According to General Mike Hyden, CIA and NSA former director, that was just normal. But the DNC attack was different. Instead of just gathering information, the hackers used the data collected and messed with the elections. They used Internet trolls to mess with the candidates' reputations — an influence campaign. In response to this, Obama acted on removing 35 Russian diplomats from the United States. All of them were spies.

But the actions Obama made were too late. Even before the elections, the government already had information about the attackers. However, they did not make it public. If they did, it would have prevented the DNC attack.

Nonetheless, it still happened. Clinton was damaged in the process, and Trump won. But it was clear as day that Putin was the main person orchestrating the attacks. It was reported by the NSA, FBI, and CIA. The possible reason Putin acted this way is that he had a lot of grudges, especially toward Clinton.

Aside from getting access from the DNC, the hackers obtained access to electoral boards. However, they did not attempt to alter the tallies. In addition to that, Russia used social media to further ignite the influence campaign.

They created accounts and pages to amplify the hatred toward immigrants, which Trump was focusing on. All of the operations were successful because they were able to hit Americans on their weakest spot.

Of course, Moscow denied all allegations, and Trump agreed.

Chapter 5: General Misha

You have the SVR and the FSB. But there is one more intelligence agency in Russia, and that is the GRU. It is the largest and most powerful of them all. And unlike the two, the structure of the GRU is unknown. It is based in a building in Moscow, which they nicknamed the Aquarium.

The Aquarium is the GRU's base, and only one American has set foot there: Michael Flynn, the former security advisor of Donald Trump. He was there to talk about leadership during his visit and was invited by Ambassador Sergio Kislyak.

Despite his known objective, which was to provide a lecture and strengthen ties with Russia to combat terrorism, many were bewildered by this move. After all, you would not see a high-ranking military advisor inside the MI6 or the DIA (Defense Intelligence Agency) to talk about leadership.

Flynn made a speech again in Cambridge in 2014. The listeners were journalists and spies — and some Russians who died mysteriously later. Another interesting thing to note is his sudden correspondence with a Russian-British woman.

Their correspondence was unclassified and they talked about Soviet history. Flynn never informed the DIA about this woman — even though protocol states that he needs to report every time he meets with a foreign national. And another interesting thing is that he used the name General Misha as his signature. Misha is the Russian equivalent of Michael.

During Flynn's stint at the DIA as chief, his subordinates and colleagues provided negative feedback about him. He was erratic, self-absorbed, obsessed with Iran, abusive, dismissive, had a confusing line of thinking, and was generally a liability.

He was removed from the DIA a year early. He was dismissed by James Clapper, director of national intelligence. Flynn blamed Obama for his removal. The DIA followed up on him two months later, that he needed to disclose any earnings he got from any foreign power.

Since his removal, he usually spent his time writing books, giving lectures, and appearing on television for interviews. One of the books he had written focused on destroying evil Islamists and Obama as one of the worst presidents in US modern history. In a nutshell, he had the same view as Trump. When Trump declared his desire to run, Flynn immediately got in contact with him and served as a consultant.

Then, Flynn was invited to attend an event in Russia. It was the tenth anniversary of RT, Russia's government-owned international television channel. There, Flynn sat beside Putin. The question on why Flynn would be there immediately sprung up. And the probable reason was that he was a close Trump ally.

Later, he would appear often in RT. When asked about being seated next to Putin, Flynn defended that he had no idea about the seating arrangement and that he did not even talk to Putin. But during his RT stint, he admitted that he had gained compensation. And according to the letter sent to him, he should have disclosed earnings from a foreign power, which he failed to do.

Early in 2016, Flynn became the foreign policy adviser to Trump. Perhaps due to the influential power of his position, he became aggressive on Twitter — just like his boss. He primarily targeted Obama and Clinton in his tirades. His tirades became even more below the belt when he appeared in the RNC's (Republican National Committee) Cleveland convention.

After the Cleveland convention, Steele sent two important memos to Fusion.

The first memo talked about who had the greatest power in the Putin circle. It was Ivanov, and he was not happy with the recent turn of events. He was the one who highly suggested that Russia deny any allegations connected to the dossier.

The second memo focused on Ivanov connecting and supporting certain American figures that were heavily involved in the elections. They were Lydon Larouche, Jill Stein, Carter Page, and Michael Flynn. After the memos were received, Trump fired Ivanov from his team.

Flynn became heavily favored in the Trump team. When Trump won the elections, Obama immediately told him that he should not hire or get Flynn. However, Trump did not heed Obama's warning, and three days later, Flynn became Trump's national security adviser. And all this time, Flynn was still communicating with Kislyak.

These activities will soon become the reasons for Flynn's downfall and for spurring the collusion investigation.

Chapter 6: He Does Bastards

Paul Manafort is a veteran political consultant. He can help politicians win elections even in great odds. One of the politicians he served was Viktor Yanukovych, former president of Ukraine, even though Yanukovych seemed destined to lose and never gain power in the country. When Luke Harding interviewed Manafort, he was fed with lies, especially with how he described Yanukovych.

It is interesting that Manafort was willing to work in Ukraine. It was a long ways off from Washington, where he was a junior lobbyist. The only conclusion was that it was all about the money. One of the first clients he had in Russia was Oleg Deripaska, with whom he had a $10 million yearly contract. The details about Manafort's work under Deripaska is still unknown.

After being in the business for some time, he met Yanukovuych. He knew his political career was over. When he met with Yanukovych, he was hired as an adviser. During this time, he worked as a low-profile adviser. Questions arose when sudden extreme changes happened within the Party of Regions, the party with which Yanukovych was affiliated.

After Harding's first interview with Manafort, he was unable to get in touch with him again despite going back and forth to Ukraine. When he saw him again delivering a speech in 2009, Manafort was unchanged, but the party he advised definitely had transformed as the prime choice of the Ukrainian people.

Despite the success of winning the election, Yanukovych proved to be much of a problem and threat later on. In late 2013 and early 2014, the Ukrainian revolution happened. It started out as a peace protest, but it became a bloody one. It forced Yanukovych out of Ukraine. And it allowed Russia to take advantage and annex Crimea.

Does this have anything to do with Manafort? Well, he did anything for money even if it meant that the politician he would help to win was a huge criminal that would cause damage to an entire country. Despite the events happening in Ukraine, Manafort stayed and helped the Party of Regions, which was now renamed Opposition Bloc.

Among all the people in Trump's team, Manafort had the greatest ties to Russia. Do note that Manafort's other clients were infamous personalities. Some of them were Ferdinand Marcos of the Philippines, Mobutu Sese Seko of Zaire, and Jonas Savimbi of Angola. All of them are considered "bastards" and dictators in their countries, yet Manafort was able to make them shine like diamonds.

One of the people who worked with Manafort vouched positive things about it. That person was Oleg Voloshin. He said that Manafort couldn't be faulted. He worked for the challenge of getting underdogs to win. It was not about the money. But according to Manafort's admittance about his earnings with the Party of Regions, he earned around $17 million in just two years.

Manafort has been connected with Trump for a long time. However, it was during the 2016 polling that Manafort contacted Trump. His pitch was that he had helped presidents win around the world. Trump was impressed. He was hired, and Manafort even said that he was willing to work without pay.

However, Manafort's position would be in danger when WikiLeaks released the DNC emails. Then The Times released the news about the Secret Ledger of the Party of Regions. In the ledger, Manafort's name appeared 22 times and the earnings he got amounted to $12.7 million, which spanned for five years. Manafort denied the information on the ledger and Trump defended him. Still, after that, he quit from Trump's team.

The previous stories about Manafort were the ones that have been publicly discussed and covered. But the dossier has a lot more to offer about the man. According to the dossier, Manafort was the central figure of the connection between Trump and Putin. Also, the release of the DNC emails in WikiLeaks was orchestrated by Russia.

Information indicated in the dossier was that the Russia issues were just there to distract people. They wanted to hide the fact that Trump was doing multiple business dealings in emerging markets and China. The deals involved a lot of kickbacks and bribes. And once exposed, it would be more damaging than the Russia collusion issues.

Going back to Manafort: He was still not off the hook. Politico pressed on the concerns revolving around him. They made a profile about Konstantin Kilimnik, a person who has worked with Manafort in Ukraine since 2005. For the past few years, the two frequently exchanged emails. The problem with this: there is a huge possibility that Kilimnik is from the GRU.

In 2017, investigations followed Manafort everywhere — even the US Treasury Department had some beef against him. Also, his denial of the ledger was coming apart. The Associated Press investigated Manafort's finances further and proved that some of the money was indeed transferred to him.

After being cornered, he admitted that the story was true but it was legitimately from political consultancy work. However, the investigation of how the money was transferred resulted into a huge mess. The money was going all around the world just to get to him. Basically, they were transferred from various shell companies.

Aside from that, Manafort has used multiple bank accounts and most of the shell companies were under tax havens. Also, he had purchased big properties in New York. It smelled a lot like freshly laundered money. And back in 2011, Yulia Tymoshenko, Yanukovych's political rival, sued Manafort. She alleged that Manafort used money to bribe corrupted Ukrainian officials using shell accounts from the US.

And there are a lot more of potential cases and rumors about Manafort. The FBI has a lot to do before they can establish a solid groundwork. At the time, James Comey, FBI director, only had four years of his ten-year term. His employment ended when Trump fired him.

Chapter 7: Tuesday Night Massacre

The FBI has usually viewed Trump as an entertaining person and never expected that he would win the elections. Now, Trump had won, and they regretted their leniency on him. Even if they did not want to dabble in politics, they were now forced to since Trump had a lot of baggage to be checked. And since most of the issues were related to Russia, they are now terribly busy.

Behind the FBI was James Comey. He is a reputable statesman — a true patriot. He does not care if he clashed with the President as long as he knows he is doing the right thing for the country. One of the most interesting quirks he has is that he tends to record everything he has done throughout the day and send copies to his colleagues in the Justice Department.

And it was noteworthy that Trump tried to gain Comey's friendship and loyalty while the latter tried to minimize the interactions with the former. The duration of the investigation might take a while, but he has declared a stubborn stance against the possible suspects that might have committed a crime with the alleged collusion.

Meanwhile, the Trump administration and Moscow started to make some effort in misdirecting the minds of the masses. Suddenly, a former CIA analyst reported to Trump that he had been a victim of wiretapping, which was ordered by Obama.

As the diversionary tactic did not work, Trump grew frustrated with Comey's investigation. He tried to fend off everything by telling the public that all of it was fake news.

On the other hand, Hillary Clinton was doing well despite the defeat. She apologized to the public about the mishap on the emails. The Senate and the House of Representatives, meanwhile, were hounding the sources of the leaks.

Amidst the investigations, Comey was questioned and interviewed left and right. Meanwhile, Steele was back from hiding and started working again on Orbis. The media had been trying to link the FBI, him, and Steele. Journalists were trying to find out if they were working together or if Steele was commissioned to create the dossier.

The FBI made some progress. They started sending subpoenas, particularly to associates of Flynn. And while Comey was doing his best to work on the case and travelling all over the country to investigate, he sighted upon the news. It was about Trump firing the FBI director. That was him.

Comey received three letters to "confirm" his termination. They were from Jeff Sessions, Rod Rosenstein, and Donald Trump. Trump's letter focused on how he was not an effective director based on his performance in the Russian collusion probe.

The letters from Sessions and Rosenstein talked about how he was ineffective in dealing with the Clinton email incident. The reasons — and reasoning behind them — were a mess. If people really believed the reason about the Clinton incident, then why now? Comey should have been fired ages ago.

Jeff Sessions, the attorney general, was unable to escape probes. He was interviewed if he had contacted anybody related to Russia. He denied that he had. However, he was found out to be in contact with Kislyak two times. He then recused himself from any case involving Russia.

This incident only made Trump appear more suspicious, and at the same time, it made him more frustrated. And because of the way he handled things, his first 100 days made history. All of his negative traits appeared one by one. And the media loved it; the Americans hated it.

He had the opportunity to make things right, especially when it came to the decision to fire Comey. He could have made the press think that he only followed the recommendations.

But he owned the decision as if it was a badge of honor. Then a few days after Comey's termination, Trump met with two Russians in the Oval Office.

The talk with the Russian visitors was leaked. Trump shared allied secrets that concerned the battle in Syria. It was a complete breach of protocol. Many people in the government were dismayed, even Republicans.

On the other hand, Comey was filled with shock and righteous anger. However, he was not going down without a fight. Because of his penchant of writing down notes, he had a complete small archive of his interactions with Trump. It became an excellent weapon of choice against a man who was unaware of processes and protocols.

The biggest part of the Comey's memo was dated February 14, 2017. Flynn resigned from office because he had lied to Vice President Mike Pence on February 13, 2017. Trump talked to Comey and asked him to let Flynn go, and reiterated that Flynn was a good guy. Not surprisingly, Comey's answer was noncommittal.

Because of the various events that have caused Americans to lose faith in the government, Rosenstein, the deputy attorney general, was pressured to do something. He appointed a special prosecutor to handle the collusion case: Robert

Mueller. Mueller is a hardened former FBI director. He has the record of having the longest tenure as an FBI director.

Then, Comey was interrogated by the Senate Intelligence Committee. He threw bombshells after bombshells to and about Trump.

Chapter 8: Collusion

One of the biggest challenges of the KGB was recruiting American sources. Ever since Ronald Reagan sat in power as POTUS, the KGB faced a threatening foe. To this effect, the KGB has performed numerous experiments and tests on how they could effectively get American sources.

Before that, they had targeted Americans who were leftists and sympathizers of the USSR. Their main entry point to a potential recruit was political belief. However, the number of Americans who fit the criteria dwindled as decades passed by. At the end of the almost countless changes in recruitment methods, they focused on individuals with dire egoistical, financial, and sexual needs.

The security records of the Eastern Bloc suggested that Trump might have been a target for recruitment since 1977. According to the Prague files that were declassified a few years ago, Trump and his Czech-born then-wife, Ivanka Zelnickova Trump, were being monitored by Czech spies.

In the next few years, Trump was approached by USSR diplomats. They flattered him and promised him business ventures. Those were effective tactics to win him over. In no time, he was invited to Moscow. It is a fact that Trump even wrote about that trip in his book.

The Soviets will do almost everything to provide their potential recruits the best experiences in the world in Moscow. After Trump's first visit to Moscow, his praise to the country was tremendous. However, it is interesting that Trump's visit were not fully covered in newspaper archives. Another interesting thing that happened is that, even though no business deals were made during his trips to Moscow, ideas of becoming president slowly enveloped Trump.

Then, his fantasizing of becoming president became widely known through newspapers. Just like his recent campaign, he focused on the American people and cutting ties with countries piggybacking on the United States. As this happened, Trump continued to visit Moscow to make "deals." However, it was always the same: nothing happened.

In the 1990s, the Soviet's new tactic on getting American sources came to fruition. They were able to recruit deep-seated officials in the CIA.

It is widely known that Trump was not always successful with all of his new business attempts. But the lesser-known fact is that Trump did not just flop in the United States. He tried to bring his failed products like the Trump Vodka to Moscow, which almost immediately failed.

It was around 2008 that the KGB took interest in Trump again. This time, he had exceedingly become a prime candidate for an agent. He was — is — financially, egotistically, and sexually needy. And his going against the president that time, Obama, whom Putin clearly dislikes, worked in Trump's favor.

During his multiple visits in Russia, Trump befriended the Agalarovs. Aras Agalarov is like Russia's Trump. He's just as showy, a real estate developer, and a millionaire/billionaire. Throughout the years of communicating and bonding in Russia, Agalarov has become close with Trump, to the point that he knows a few of Trump's dirtiest secrets.

The Trumps and Agalarovs became close family friends. In fact, Donald Trump Jr. has visited and stayed longer in Russia than his father. And he frequently gets in touch with Emin Agalarov, Aras' son and pop singer.

Aside from Emin, Trump Jr. also became close to Emin's publicist and music promoter, Rob Goldstone. Trump Jr. and Goldstone frequently exchanged emails. And one of those emails was a delicate one that could have easily ruined Trump's campaign if it was brought to light earlier.

The email contained an offer about providing dirt on Hilary Clinton. The full context of the message was that the Agalarovs and the Russian government were willing to help Trump win by smearing Clinton's reputation. Some of the dirt included Clinton's dealings with Russia.

The conversation about that topic continued until Trump Jr. agreed to meet up with Goldstone and the Russian attorneys behind the offer. Also, Goldstone was a huge liability. He did not know how to be discreet, to the point that he even used the subject line "Russia-Clinton private and confidential" as a header to their conversations. The meeting went through.

The email conversations were discovered in July 2017. It was already too late; Trump was already president. Before it was revealed to the public, Trump Jr. had denied his connections with Russians and the help that his father got from them.

Trump Jr. admitted them later when he found out that the news outlets already had the email. Still, he denied that they willingly took the offer. Manafort and Jared Kushner, Trump's son-in-law, denied that they saw the emails. However, even if they denied everything to their grave, their actions were a clear act of collusion with the Russians.

The White House did what Trump Jr. did. They denied everything first. Then they agreed. Then they told details that were already out in the public.

Chapter 9: Thralldom

The G20 was a much-awaited event in Germany. However, the people have a different reason for waiting. Instead of wanting to know what the topic big nations would talk about, they waited for Trump and Putin. The G20 would be their first meeting after Trump became the president of the United States.

Some were disappointed, but those people in the G20 event, particularly the press, were dumbfounded by the things they witnessed. The two met cordially and did not interact that much — onscreen. They did not also actively avoid each other. Their actions were simply of "regular" world leaders. The highest point was when Trump gave his infamous handshake to Putin. Aside from the meeting, the protests outside became the primary concern.

When Trump had the chance to talk with Putin, he never actively said anything about the recently discovered Russian hackings and other potential Russian interference with US politics. To add insult to injury, the two had agreed upon to team up in fighting cyber-attacks and crimes.

From the perspective of the Trump skeptic, Trump just

accepted the denials that Russia made about the attacks. It also made Trump an easy pawn for the Russians. The current administration of the United States was the perfect opportunity for Russia to exploit.

Another high point in the G20 summit was when Trump went his way around to talk to Putin. After almost ignoring most of the other leaders present — even if they were allies — he only talked to Putin. What transpired in that conversation is virtually unknown to anyone, including the US government.

Aside from Trump being "too close" to Putin, he even disparaged NATO. In addition, his speech made the NATO nations feel that the United States was not committing to collective defense. And who cannot forget that he mentioned that other NATO nations should "pay up" because they owed massive amounts of funds. The cherry on the top was when he pushed away Montenegro's prime minister, Dusko Markovic.

These actions of Trump are baffling its allies in NATO. Other countries are already questioning his allegiance. Behind the scenes, Trump's stance was favorable to Russia. After all, one of its prime goals is the dissolution of NATO.

One of the prominent figures that felt the United States was falling apart is Angela Merkel, Germany's chancellor. She already knew about the frequent connection between Trump and Russia. She had been directly informed of it.

Also, she knew that Russia actually did the hacking in the DNC. It was not the first time. Russian hackers have been testing and attacking multiple countries, particularly in Estonia and France.

During his campaign and first few weeks as POTUS, Trump seemed like a nation-builder. However, it suddenly changed. He focused on increasing the American force outside the country. Together with that, the recent white supremacist protest allowed people to see Trump as a supporter and sympathizer of neo-Nazis.

What's more, climate change, to him, is a hoax. And since Russian hackers disrupted the country, the legislation passed a bill to apply sanctions to Russia. Trump was forced to sign it because of the large support in the Senate and Congress, but he hated it. This action forced more than 700 Russian diplomats out of the country.

Russia countered this move and sent US diplomats back, too. Instead of retaliating and getting upset, Trump was glad. He even thanked Putin because the employees on payroll would be reduced. Of course, it does not work like that. Those people who will be sent home will still be on payroll.

These events all show one thing: Putin was easily manhandling Trump.

Trump does not view Russia as an enemy. What and who he does view as an enemy is Mueller. While the special counsel continues snooping for information on what happened, the president is constantly lying and concealing facts.

Mueller is bad news for Trump. First, he is a seasoned veteran. Second, he has some solid team members that are known to catch big fish. And third, the FBI has negative feelings toward Trump because of what he did to James Comey. One of the great displays of Mueller's team capability was when it raided Manafort's home by surprise.

Chapter 10: From Russia with Cash

One possible method that Russia employed to send money to Trump was to buy property. One of these properties is the Palm Beach mansion in Florida. In 2008, it was sold to Dmitry Rybolovlev, a potash magnate in Russia. The sale cost $95 million. It was too expensive.

The funny thing was that Rybolovlev never used it. The only time he was there was when he wanted to look at the house. He even demolished it. He did not even let his family use it. His daughter rented an apartment in the United States when she was in college.

It is known to many that Rybolovlev does not want to waste money, so why would he bother getting a property that was not really that valuable? Yes, the Palm Beach mansion is grand, but it would barely amount to the cash that Rybolovlev used to buy it.

On a different note, Rybolovlev is a person of interest. From 2016 to 2017, the potash magnate has been frequently moving around the United States using his private jet. And "coincidentally" his plane is always where Trump's was.

Even though the two never met when their planes appeared

on the same airport, it is speculated that Dmitry is meeting Trump's lawyer, Michael Cohen. According to the dossier, he was a secret intermediary for Trump's under-the-table deals. It is speculated that Russia is using Rybolovlev as the delivery guy for Trump. When approached about the contents of the dossier, Cohen immediately denied everything.

Investigative reporters tried their best to get all information about Rybolovlev and Trumps' flights. They found no solid connections. According to the man's adviser, Rybolovlev is just in the United States usually for business and pleasure. Another piece of information that the adviser provided is that his boss did not know Trump intimately.

Rybolovlev often used shell companies and tax havens to increase his wealth. Also, he took advantage of the Bank of Cyprus. He is one of its biggest investors. It is interesting to note that other investors of the bank are mostly high-profile Russians. And a unique investor there is an American who goes by the name Wilbur Ross.

He became the chief shareholder of the bank and then the vice chairman. During his stint there, he primarily worked with Russians who have close ties to Putin. In 2017, he resigned from the bank. Then he became Trump's secretary of commerce.

Trump also has a connection in Cyprus — so did Manafort. In 2008, Trump established two companies in Cyprus. One of them was Trump Construction Co. Ltd. Its activities are unknown to the public.

Eurasians and Russians have been buying properties from Trump ever since. Some of them are legitimate, but most are connected to Russian organized crime groups. When Trump was having financial troubles, Russian immigrants bought his properties.

For the past few years, Trump properties have been connected to Russian criminals. For example, Vyacheslav Ivankov, a Russian mafia and Moscow felon, has been found in a luxury unit in Trump Tower. The FBI was surprised. It even took them three years before they pinpointed Ivankov's location.

Chapter 11: The Strange Case of the German Bank

In 2005, Trump borrowed $640 million from Deutsche Bank. After three years and the financial crash, Trump defaulted. This forced the bank to create a motion of summary judgment. It pushed Trump to pay the remaining $330 million.

Trump refused to pay. He blamed the crash and called it force de majeure. Because of that, he was not liable to pay the amount he owed. And to make matters worse, he said that the bank should pay him instead. He sued the bank for $3 billion in damages.

This behavior from Trump was the reason most national banks do not allow him to make a loan. And actually, his reaction to Deutsche Bank did not happen because of the financial crash. It is actually his protocol. He has already discussed much of these tactics in the books he has authored.

Deutsche Bank acquired an affidavit against Trump, which was filed in New York. They did their research. The attorney who was handling the case was probably smirking when he got a hold of the affidavit. In the writ, Trump boasted that he was rich — that he was the ultimate deal-maker without any peers. He even said that he is worth billions of dollars.

One can easily question why this billionaire cannot even pay the three hundred million and would even attempt to countersue with a price tag of three billion. The bank already expected this from Trump. However, they did not anticipate how much worse he could be.

Of course, the judge rejected Trump's case. The bank still proceeded to get its money from Trump. Trump did pay. However, things got crazier. He acquired a loan to pay the money back. The lender? The same bank, Deutsche Bank, but a different division.

The one he had trouble with was the real estate division. The one who saved him was the private wealth division. Aside from having a tremendous debt over at another division, the private wealth division focused on catering to high net worth individuals and shunned away from property-related loans — that is why they have a real estate division after all. But despite those facts, Trump was still provided with money. And after the fiasco, the same division also credited him with up to $50 million dollars.

Trump was the first president that got elected with huge sums of debt. The debt he has accumulated is due on 2023 to

2024. His campaign accentuated that he is a rich guy and great deal-maker, and so most people believe that he is doing well in the money department. On the other hand, people are alarmed that he has power now. He can easily use his position to get back to the people he owes money to.

The ones in Deutsche Bank in New York were flabbergasted. How could that happen? And that was not all. The bank suddenly got a branch in Moscow and even got a deal with a state development bank, Vnesheconombank, or VEB. Then, the branch performed too well. An unheard performance in Russian history.

Speculations say that the bank is busy laundering money. And the amount it was processing was in billions. The money easily flowed from Russia, London, New York, and back. The bank also made a connection with Vneshtorgbank — another state-owned bank that is closely tied to the intelligence networks in Russia.

Other Russian banks were suspicious of Deutsche Bank. Being a bank outside of the country and having close connections to two state-owned banks — it was fishy. Not to mention that its performance easily got boosted.

Too many questions are being begged to be answered. Yet any attempts to know what happened with Trump's case and loans in Deutsche Bank failed. There are many possibilities, but the Russian part of all things weighs a lot.

In the coming months, suspicion on Deutsche Bank piled on more and more. The laundering business got larger and involved multiple banks and flowed into different countries. And as always, it was Deutsche Bank that was alleged to be the entry point of all dirty monies that would be "washed."

Other intelligence networks also looked into this and how Trump, in the midst of a financial crisis with no one in the United States willing to provide a loan to him, was still operating in fine condition.

On the other hand, it was not just Donald Trump that Deutsche Bank favored. Most of his family members received preferential treatment from the bank.

The Department of Financial Services also joined the fray. And since Trump has entered politics, his financial activities have been of interest. Primarily, the DFS wanted to know if Trump was receiving Russian money.

The DFS got nothing. There was no trail leading back to Russia. However, when Deutsche Bank was asked again about its review of Trump's finances, it kept mum. And as usual, Trump would not even provide any hints about his tax filings.

Multiple questions, again, left unanswered. The first one: is Trump really rich? Second, is he receiving financial aid from Russia? Third, was Deutsche Bank compromised by Russia already? It is really up to Mueller and his FBI cohorts to clear everything up.

Epilogue

Despite boasting that he has done the most out of all the presidents, Trump's first year in office is riddled with incompetence. If people will try to think of the things he did in the office, they will think of golf and tweeting.

The White House, on the other hand, is drowning in multiple issues. Some are trivial. Some are crucial. And most were created by themselves. Most of the effort of the current administration was used to create cover-ups and look for ways on how they could reverse the damages the president had made.

Now, the special counsel is just behind him. They are investigating every nook and cranny. And once they are finished, someone will definitely get punished by the law. Right now, Manafort and Flynn are receiving all the heat behind the scenes. The opposition is just waiting patiently for the FBI to reel in the biggest fish.

On Steele's end, the release of the dossier would have meant great success for Moscow. Even if the dossier has not yet been completely proven to be factual, the allegations and conspiracies are holding everybody back in making a move.

However, there is still a chance that all of this will be forgotten and the ones responsible for all the shenanigans to get away scot-free. And that will happen if the FBI does not catch up with the investigation.

Notes on Sources

Luke Harding gets all information first hand. And it does not matter where or when he is getting his information. It can be anytime and anywhere. Most of his sources make a living in the intelligence industry.

As his progress on investigating and documenting this issue grew, more sources willingly offered him information. When it comes to the vivid description of Russia, his experience is a reliable source. He has lived there as a journalist for more than four years.

Conclusion

Do note that some parts of this book are not completely factual. Some are theories and some are circumstantial conclusions. Nonetheless, most of the events, especially in Trump's side, are real.

One of the key takeaways here is that the spy business is far different from what you see in the movies. You do not have a license to kill and you do not need to infiltrate a top-secret area to get information. Most of the spies involved in this book are mostly diplomats. They do not even actively do active spying. They mostly stay in their assigned location and gradually create a network of intelligent sources.

Second, it becomes easy to question the wealth of rich people, especially if a rich person's name is Donald Trump. He has displayed and elevated himself as one of the wealthiest men and the best deal-maker in the world. Having overcome multiple bankruptcies and outrun his debts, you have to wonder if the things he did to recover were possible in the legal realm.

Third, the people of the United States are flawed. Can you imagine that Trump voters were played like fiddles by Russia and Manafort and company? Can you imagine how a completely ineffectual person can reach the highest position in the most powerful country in the world?

And do you feel betrayed? Betrayed that the man you trusted to make America great again is primarily working for his, his cohorts', and Russia's gain? Are you okay that the tax you pay is not even going back to you or your children?

Fourth, it is truly amazing how flattery, money, and sex can make someone relinquish their patriotism. Can you see that each person in the world has a price tag? And once paid, that person would be willing to sell everything off, even if it meant that his country and his children's future would be jeopardized?

Fifth, politics is truly a dirty game to play. And it does not have any room for novices and morons. And the funny thing is that, when a politician loses in the game, it's the people who have to suffer.

Those are just a few thoughts that should challenge your thinking when it comes to the current state of affairs in the United States. Of course, those thoughts are relatively biased depending on who is reading this. But it is important that you consider them.

Hopefully, in the coming weeks or months, the issue about

the alleged Russian collusion would be done and dealt with. There is no reason that the government waste time finding fault and lying about the truth. There are more immediate issues in this country that should be prioritized.

Lastly, here's to hoping that all those involved in this case would turn up and be honest. They should forget about their own motives and selfish desires. It is not the right time to engage in partisan politics and argue who are Republicans and Democrats. The US has a bigger opposition on the other side of the world, and it is much better if all Americans work towards defending the country's sovereignty, democracy, and good relationship with other countries.

Final Thoughts

Hey! Did you enjoy this book? We sincerely hope you thoroughly enjoyed this short read and have gotten immensely valuable insights that will help you in any areas of your life.

Would it be too greedy if we ask for a review from you?

It takes 1 minute to leave 1 review to possibly influence 1 more person's decision to read just 1 book which may change their 1 life. Your 1 minute matters and we value it and thank you so much for giving us your 1 minute. If it sucks, just say it sucks. Period.

FREE BONUS

<u>P.S. Is it okay if we overdeliver?</u>

Here at Abbey Beathan Publishing, we believe in overdelivering way beyond our reader's expectations. Is it okay if we overdeliver?

Here's the deal, we're going to give you an extremely valuable cheatsheet of "Accelerated Learning". We've partnered up with Ikigai Publishing to present to you the exclusive bonus of "Accelerated Learning Cheatsheet"

What's the catch? We need to trust you… You see, we want to overdeliver and in order for us to do that, we've to trust our reader to keep this bonus a secret to themselves. Why? Because we don't want people to be getting our exclusive accelerated learning cheatsheet without even buying our books itself. Unethical, right?

Ok. Are you ready?

Simply Visit this link: http://bit.ly/acceleratedcheatsheet

We hope you'll enjoy our free bonuses as much as we've enjoyed preparing it for you!

Free Bonus #2: Free Book Preview of Summary: A Gentleman in Moscow

The Book at a Glance

The book begins with an account of Count Alexander Ilyich Rostov's appearance before the Emergency Committee of the People's Commissariat for Internal Affairs on the 21st of June in 1992.

The story that ensues is a story of a man's adventures within the four walls of the hotel, destined to be his home forever.

BOOK ONE

Chapter 1: 1922: An Ambassador

Count Alexander Ilyich Rostov, after receiving his sentence to live and stay in the Metropol forever, came back to his hotel room only to find that he would be transferring from his third-floor suite to the attic in the sixth floor.

Chapter 2: An Anglican Shore

The Count reminisces about his old days as he reads the *Essays of Michel Montaigne*, noting that he now has more time to read the book given his new circumstances.

Chapter 3: An Appointment

The Count eagerly waits for his 12 o'clock appointment with the Metropol's barber, Yaroslov.

Chapter 4: An Acquaintanceship

As he dines alone in the Piazza, the Count is approached by nine-year-old Nina Kulikova, daughter of a widowed Ukrainian bureaucrat.

Chapter 5: Anyway …

Nina formally invites the Count for an afternoon tea to discuss the rules of being a princess.

Chapter 6: Around and About

Nina takes the Count exploring and educates him about every inch of the hotel.

Chapter 7: An Assembly

The Count and Nina spy on the Assembly from the balcony of the ballroom hall.

Chapter 8: Archeologies

The Count was visited by Mishka, a friend he met in the Imperial University.

Chapter 9: Advent

It was Christmas Eve, when the Count ate dinner alone, went back to his room, and waited until midnight to open Nina's present.

BOOK TWO

Chapter 1: An Actress, An Apparition, An Apiary

The Count had an unpleasant encounter with a willowy woman, movie star Anna Kurokova, in the hotel lobby. She invited him for dinner in her suite later that evening.

Chapter 2: Addendum

Anna Kurokova could not brush aside what the Count did before he left her room the night they had dinner together.

Chapter 3: 1924: Anonymity

The Count thinks that he had seemingly become invisible in the eyes of his friends and acquaintances.

Chapter 4: 1926: Adieu

The Count prepares for his last day and spends his last moments in a bar where he engages in a conversation with two travelers.

BOOK THREE

Chapter 1: 1930

The Count begins his day by preparing breakfast, eating, and exercising.

Chapter 2: Arachne's Art

The Count has since learned how to sew, citing the need for him to always appear well-groomed in his uniform.

Chapter 3: An Afternoon Assignation

Ever since her career plummeted, Anna Urbanova has been frequenting the Boyarsky to meet with directors she used to know. After dinner with her guests, she would slip into her room and wait for the Count.

Chapter 4: An Alliance

The Count was invited to a private dinner by a Party Official, who asked him to teach him the English and French language.

Chapter 5: Absinthe

The Count heads to the bar to ask for absinthe, the fifteenth ingredient needed for the Boyarsky triumvirate's grand plan.

Chapter 6: Addendum

Nina along with her friends heads off to the country's agricultural regions.

Chapter 7: An Arrival

The Count was taken by surprise when Nina showed up in the Metropol asking him to take care of her child while she sets off to find her husband who has been jailed.

Chapter 8: Adjustments

The Count struggles with the quiet child, but manages slowly to engage her in a conversation.

Chapter 9: Ascending, Alighting

The Count spends the day managing Sofia and working around his tight schedule. As he tries to fall asleep that night, he is drowned with concern for his friends who are all facing difficulties in their lives.

Chapter 10: Addendum

Sofia wakes up the Count, telling him that she had left her doll in Marina's office.

Chapter 11: 1946

A lone man observes the line of people waiting to pay their respects to Lenin. He notes how little has changed of the city, and remembers how five years ago the city was almost conquered by Germans.

Chapter 12: Antics, Antitheses, an Accident

The Count's day started with him witnessing a goose chase on the fourth floor, to meeting his long-time friend Mishka, to a heated discussion with Osip. The day however, was concluded when Sofia fell down the stairs and the Count rushed her to the hospital to receive surgery.

Chapter 13: Addendum

Andrey heads back home after visiting Sofia from the hospital. He reminisces about his son who died in the war.

BOOK FOUR

Chapter 1: Adagio, Andante, Allegro

The Count discovers that Sofia has been studying the piano, and as a matter of fact, was incredibly good.

Chapter 2: America

The Count was having dinner with Sofia when the matter of his secret relationship with Anna Urbanova was brought up.

Chapter 3: Apostles and Apostates

Sofia and Anna Urbanova came home from Sofia's school competition, with Anna happily announcing that Sofia had won. While the others headed downstairs to continue the celebration, the Count stayed behind to confer with Katerina, Mishka's old lover.

BOOK FIVE

Chapter 1: 1954: Applause and Acclaim

The Count heard from Viktor Stepanovich that Sofia withdrew from the orchestra's tour. That night, while they were having dinner, the Count managed to convince Sofia to reconsider.

Chapter 2: Achilles Agonistes

The Count helps Sofia make the necessary preparations for her departure in a few months.

Chapter 3: Arrivederci

The Count enters the room of an Italian couple and steals a pair of pants and a white oxford.

Chapter 4: Adulthood

Sofia wears the gown that Marina made for her and shows it off to the Count and Anna.

Chapter 5: An Announcement

The Count was tasked to oversee the most important dinner of the year.

Chapter 6: Anecdotes

On the night of her departure, Sofia and the Count had a private dinner in the study.

Chapter 7: An Association

Not having seen each other in a long time, Osip and the Count decided to meet the next week to watch Casablanca.

Chapter 8: Antagonists at Arms (And an Absolution)

The Count locked the Bishop in a room in the basement after the latter was found poking through the maps of Paris on the Count's desk.

Chapter 9: Apotheoses

After months of planning, today would be the day that Alexander Rostov leaves the Metropol.

AFTERWORD

Afterwards

The following morning, officers went to the Metropol to

question Alexander Rostov regarding his missing daughter. Alexander, however, was missing and the manager that they found locked in the basement revealed that Alexander had been conspiring to leave all along.

And Anon

Alexander Rostov visits his old home and then walks five miles away to an inn where a willowy woman waits for him.

SUMMARY:

Cosmos

The Book

ABBEY BEATHAN

damages or injury caused by the use and application, whether directly or indirectly, of any advice or information presented, whether for breach of contract, tort, negligence, personal injury, criminal intent, or under any other cause of action.

You agree to accept all risks of using the information presented inside this book. You need to consult a professional medical practitioner in order to ensure you are both able and healthy enough to participate in this program.

Table of Contents

The Book at a Glance

Our world is just a mere shore, we wonder how deep the cosmic ocean is.

The world is a small place compared to the universe. The universe is ever expanding, ever wondered what is beyond or world? Ever wondered about what lies beyond this small planet of ours? What is the cosmos? Why is it so vast? Our knowledge of the cosmos is just miniscule, just barely scratching the surface. This book will question everyone about their own existence and ideas, as well as to awaken their inner philosophers.

I.   The Shores of the Cosmic Ocean

A human's knowledge is much more limited than you think it is. Be curious about your own existence. Wonder about everything beyond our grasp, be a philosopher and question our own limited knowledge.

II.   One Voice in the Cosmic Fugue

A voice, a single voice in the vast cosmic ocean is all that we hear. When will we be able to hear a symphony? A living choir of exploration and discovery? Are we only limited with knowing our own species? Or will we be able to step up and improve our own auditory senses?

III. The Harmony of Worlds

Harmony, the opposite of chaos. When will we be able to unite this chaotic world with humans that are all separated by different barriers? Is there a way to unite all races regardless of barriers? Is the cosmos itself a significant help for harmonious relationships of all races?

IV. Heaven and Hell

The person that cared for us so dearly, will be willing to punish us if we are disobedient children. A mother's love is so great that she will help us and nurture us for everything the future will give to us. Our mother loves us so much that she is willing to hurt us for us to learn our mistakes. Our mistakes can be so great, that it will hurt our very own mother.

V. Blues for a Red Planet

What a great sight to behold, a great hulking mass of chaos. A chaos that is once known as harmony, said to have lifeforms dwelling in it. Exploring this planet is an easy task being our neighbor, only to be disappointed because of failure to prove various theories and speculations about this planet.

VI. Travelers' Tales

Voyagers, explorers, travelers, they all have tales. Their story is passed down upon generations to signify the importance of their work and discoveries. Ever wondered about the tales of a space voyager? Ever wondered what is like to go on a space adventure? An adventure full of excitement and risks towards a great ball of chaos circling our sun.

VII. The Backbone of Night

The main picture of the night. What are those glittering lights? Is this a dream? Are those shimmering lights the backbone of the night as well as its definition? Why are there lights in the night? How are they formed?

VIII.   Travels in Space and Time

The greatest stories came from far away, the most epic expeditions are done with the greatest risks. What are these expeditions? Ever wondered about every expedition that helped shaped our knowledge to what it is today?

IX. The Lives of the Stars

The stars, the backbone of the night. What are they? These lights are above, shimmering for our eyes to behold. When will they stop shimmering? Are they there forever in the sky?

X.   The Edge of Forever

The edge of infinity. There is none, the sky is endless, boundless, infinite. Constantly expanding as time goes by.

Like the mathematical constant Pi, the cosmos is never ending. It goes on and on with no end. With such infinite expansion, edges are nowhere to be find. What are its limits however? What are the limits of our own understanding of the cosmos itself?

XI. The Persistence of Memory

Memories, they all fade away. This significant information will inevitably be lost in the echo of countless voices in the sea of humanity. Is there a way to store such information? Is there a way for a memory to not just fade away? Will information linger forever? Will us humans be able to have our mark in this universe? Will our history persist through the ends of time?

XII. Encyclopaedia Galactica

What does it feel like when we are a part of a book? A book where every lifeform in the universe is listed with information about them. What does it feel like if our species are a part of something big? What does other beings think of us? Are we much more different from their perspective?

XIII. Who Speaks for Earth?

Earth is a fragile place with chaotic origins. We are intelligent beings and yet we are naïve at the same time. We are Earth's representatives however, and we represent the overall state of life on Earth. So far, we are also the greatest creation of the cosmos. We are the most intelligent beings at the moment, unless we discover and communicate with other intelligent lifeforms in the cosmos.

Chapter 1: The Shores of the Cosmic Ocean

The first men to be created and formed were called the Sorcerer of Fatal Laughter, the Sorcerer of Night, Unkempt, and the Black Sorcerer ... They were endowed with intelligence, they succeeded in knowing all that there is in the world. When they looked, instantly they saw all that is around them, and they contemplated in turn the arc of

heaven and the round face of the earth ... [Then the Creator said]: "They know all ... what shall we do with them now? Let their sight reach only to that which is near; let them see only a little of the face of the earth!... Are they not by nature simple creatures of

our making? Must they also be gods?"

—The Popol Vuh of the Quiché Maya

The known is finite, the unknown infinite; intellectually we stand on an islet in the midst of an illimitable ocean of inexplicability. Our business in every generation is to reclaim a little more land.

—T. H. Huxley, 1887

This world we live in is just a small puzzle piece in the vast Cosmic Ocean. A single puzzle piece where only a miniscule portion of the universe is seen.

The cosmic ocean is all that is or there was or there ever will be. Our feeble understanding of the Cosmos moves us- our perception, imagination and other senses, as if we are approaching the unthinkable, the greatest of mysteries.

The size of the cosmos is beyond human imagination, in a cosmic perception, human actions and conscience seem petty and insignificant. We only know the cosmos as the far great reaches of the universe, farther than a human mind could handle. Our species however, are young, brilliant, intelligent, bold and curious. Showing great promise, our future depends on our knowledge about the cosmic ocean.

The cosmic ocean calls to us, great ambitions of discovery and exploration is promising however, our own reach is only within the shore of the great cosmic ocean itself- our own little home.

The Earth's surface is the shore of the vast cosmic ocean. Because of being Earth's inhabitants, we have already explored a majority of the shore. Waddling and damping our toes to the sea tempts us to explore the whole cosmic ocean.

The Cosmos is large indeed, even familiar distance units used in Earth cannot be applied in exploring the Cosmos. Instead, we measure distance using the speed of light. The speed of light travels 186,000 miles in one second and 6 trillion miles in a year. That unit, the distance that light travels in a year, is called a light-year.

In the whole universe, there are approximately billions of galaxies, our local group of galaxies however only comprises of 20 galaxies. An example of a galaxy part of the local group is the M31, near our own galaxy, the Milky Way.

These galaxies have a vast array of luminous self-sustained stars. Stars on which different celestial bodies surround them. Some stars are so close to each other that starstuff flows between them, some stars are invisible by being a black hole, some stars are larger than Jupiter and are called as supernova, some shine mainly through infrared and visible light, some are great sources of x-rays, some are blue young stars, some are also red old stars, other flicker uncertainly and small white or black stars are close to dying. There are a huge number of stars, but we only know one, our own Sun.

We have reached our own backyard; the Sun is surrounded by celestial bodies that are made up of different molecules. The sun is also surrounded by giant snowballs composed of ice and rock and some other molecules. A passing star gives gravitational tug, allowing these snowballs to be near our Sun. Heated, the ice in the snowballs will vaporize, and a wonderful cometary tail develops.

We have approached the planets of our solar system, the planets of which we have set our eyes upon. Our planet Earth is beautiful, full of lifeforms, the proof that the cosmos is alive indeed.

That discovery that the Earth is little dates back to ancient Near East, also called as the Third Century. Eratosthenes concluded that the Earth is round, spherical based on his observations with the rays of our sun.

Since then, many brave voyagers set sailed to prove the claim. Many lands were conquered and discovered, thus further expanding our knowledge about Earth.

Hipparchus, Euclid, Eratosthenes, Herophilon and many more, they all helped in discovering Planet Earth and the solar system.

The thing is, the cosmos is made up of various matter and energy that we cannot comprehend. We refer to these things as "dark". Every area in the universe is brimming with various unknown matter and energy so leading us to wonder, where is everyone?

With the vastness of the cosmos, with the matter and energy composing it, the sheer amount materials within our cosmos is enough to fill the universe with life, but why are there no lifeforms around our neighborhood?

Is it with every second, the percentage of us taking up an area of the cosmos is becoming even more miniscule, even lessening the chance to find a lifeform in other areas of the universe because of the expansion of the cosmos decreasing that chance.

Wonder, for we are just a feeble creation of it so far.

The cosmos is vast yes, but one thing is for sure, we are the most spectacular of all of its creations so far.

Chapter 2: One Voice in the Cosmic Fugue

Probably all the organic beings which have ever lived on this earth have descended from some one primordial form, into which life was first breathed.... There is grandeur in this view of life ... that, whilst this planet has gone cycling on according to the fixed law of gravity, from so simple a beginning endless forms most beautiful and most wonderful have been, and are being, evolved.

—Charles Darwin, *The Origin of Species*, 1859

Humans are curious beings; their intelligence enables us to be on top of every organism in the planet. The thing is, how have we come about? Are there also intelligent lifeforms or even rudimentary lifeforms in other planets? We have already discovered that there are microorganisms hiding in organic matter scattered throughout our solar system so what are the odds of finding similar lifeforms like those of Earth in other planets?

Are the odds small? Miniscule? Are the chances smaller than an atom? Even then, we should continue finding another voice within the cosmos. Even if it takes longer than everything in our time.

But then, we are very limited here in our planet. Our knowledge is only within the reaches of our own shore, not even exceeding it. Our Science only deals with here, only with the study of organisms living in here, what if there are other lifeforms? The study of life will exceed new heights because of the discovery of other lifeforms triggering us humans to increase our standards and to improve our own technology for the benefit of knowledge and wisdom.

Lifeforms engage in various methods to adapt and survive in the ever-changing environments of planet Earth. Methods such as artificial selection is implemented to produce greater breed of organisms. Artificial Selection helped in domesticating different breeds of animals such as cats and dogs. It is used for efficient breeding and to prevent defects. Nature also has its own method of selection called natural selection. The breed that survives the ever-changing world of ours will be the finest breed. Each generation will improve to suit their needs for the current age.

Natural selection is also the mechanism that drives evolution. Charles Darwin and Alfred Russel Wallace discovered this fact. They stated that nature will always change and thus, the species that are better suited for survival will be fit to live more than species which are not adapting to change.

Mutations, are genetic changes that enable a species to adapt.

Mutation provides the raw material for evolution, without it, evolution is nothing.

There was a time when the Drosophila moth piqued my interests. An adult moth in the Drosophila laboratories. Instead of wanting the fruit flies themselves, the female moth instead placed her eggs in molasses. Right before my eyes, I just witnessed an adaptation by the moth.

The secrets of evolution are off death and time. There are an enormous number of lifeform deaths throughout the passing of time, mainly because of the fact that these lifeforms imperfectly adapted to the environment.

Evolution, since the dawn of time is a prerequisite for all lifeforms to exist. When Earth was still an infant, there are different lifeforms that were developed. These lifeforms adapted to Earth's harsh climate and environment perfectly. As Earth cooled however, these lifeforms were definitely having a hard time coping to such environment. The adapted, evolved to fit themselves to their new environment. Since then, as Earth's environment and atmosphere changed, so as the inhabiting lifeforms. Evolution has a long history throughout since the dawn of time. Even the DNA in our cells might be a product of evolution. The long evolutionary separation of the genetic codes of mitochondria and the nuclei is an evidence that mitochondria were once free-living organisms incorporated into the cell in a symbiotic relationship billions of years ago. This may be the reason why there is a prolific development of many-celled organisms in the Cambrian era.

With this, history is not just for events, history is needed to track down the origins, the process of evolution of a lifeform. We need this to study and improve our knowledge for future generations of our species.

Biology is more than just the study of life, it is also the study of life's history. We have only heard voices of life on one feeble world. But we only have yet to listen for other voices in the Cosmic Fugue. These voices in unison is an orchestra, when is the time that we will conduct an orchestra of various lifeforms? A symphony of life in the cosmos.

Chapter 3: The Harmony of Worlds

We do not ask for what useful purpose the birds do sing, for song is their pleasure since they were created for singing. Similarly, we ought not to ask why the human mind troubles to fathom the secrets of the heavens.... The diversity of the phenomena of Nature is so great, and the treasures hidden in the heavens so rich, precisely in order that the human mind shall never be lacking in fresh nourishment.

—Johannes Kepler, *Mysterium Cosmographicum*

Change is a necessity for exploration and development, without it, there are none to do in this world. We need to gather wisdom and knowledge for the improvement and survival of our own species. Change is an improvement, change is a need for survival. Our survival instinct enables us to be more humane, to have concern for our species' survival for we have only yet to leave a mark in the cosmos.

Understanding the world is human nature, curiosity plays a big part in it. Every philosophical idea is started by curiosity. In the old times, when we have yet to discover the stars in the sky, we are curious, wondering about what are those shimmering dots in the sky. That is a time when people used to look up in the night sky, wandering about the patterns of the glowing dots, wandering about what is beyond our little world. Wandering about the height of our own civilization, the limits of our intelligence.

These dots are also used by many people for various purposes such as navigation and measuring the passing of seasons. Through instruments made by our ancestors, seasons can be predicted.

Knowing and predicting seasons is a necessity to predict various variables in our world. Things such as the harvesting of crops rely on predicting seasons to have efficient harvesting. All of the heavenly bodies, the stars, planets, the moon, the sun, these have connections to our world.

Astrology is the study of the movements of celestial bodies while astronomy is the study of celestial bodies. More people are inclined towards astrology because of our ancestor's belief that these celestial bodies affects the destiny and fate of a person. The ecstasy of knowing your destiny is exciting, more than studying the evolution and history of celestial bodies.

In ancient times, Chinese astrologers were to be executed if their predictions are inaccurate, prompting them to just edit the records so that their predictions will align with reality, preventing execution because of inaccurate predictions.

Throughout years of observation and discovery, astrology has evolved to be somewhat of a combination of mathematics, fraud, and fuzzy thinking.

In the modern age, with modern equipment and various mistakes from the past, it can be noticed that astrological predictions shall be taken with a grain of salt. We humans, yearn to have a connection with the heavens, to see a bigger picture with our feeble minds as seen with the various celestial bodies imprinted on various national flags. We want to be part of a bigger picture, we want to know and change our destiny and fate for our own selfish desires.

Modern popular astrology runs back to Ptolemy, where he and his colleagues already discovered some astrological phenomena such as equinoxes, quasars, celestial bodies, pulsars, exploding galaxies, symbiotic stars, cataclysmic variables, and X-ray sources – all of which are discovered during Ptolemy's time using practical methods and instruments. Using practical methods and instruments for discovery is unusual, however it worked because of determination, intelligence, and teamwork.

Modern astrologers pay almost no attention to this knowledge, astrology became a pseudoscience, while astronomy became the fruits of Ptolemy's time. Astronomy and astrology are indistinctive during Ptolemy's time, unlike now in the current era, with the help of modern technology, distinctions of both is clear for all humans to know.

Ptolemy believed in Earth being the center of the universe, because of this, our solar system used to be geocentric, with the sun and other planets rotating around the Earth in a circular motion.

Nicholas Copernicus rejected the idea however, and instead hypothesized that the solar system is heliocentric, the sun placed at the middle while all the planets revolve around it. The Earth is demoted to being the third planet nearest to the sun from being the center of the solar system.

Nicholas' proposition was rejected outright by various astronomers of his time because of Ptolemy's discovery is being more widely accepted by then.

Martin Luther also described him as "an upstart astrologer, a fool wishing to reverse the entire concept of astrology. But, the Sacred Scripture tells us   that he commanded the Sun to stand still, not the Earth."

The debate on whether the solar system is geocentric or heliocentric reached its climax in the 16th century with Johannes Kepler.

Johannes Kepler is a bright but a troublesome student, a curious individual wishing to know about the world that his God has made for him and his species.

Questioning and theorizing the Pythagorean solids, about whether these solids align with the movements of planets, is the height of his curiosity.

He attempted to propose a research grant to the Duke of Württemberg, offering to supervise the construction of his solids. His proposal was rejected and was told to first construct a less expensive version out of paper.

Days and nights he attempted to prove his hypothesis but, it all failed until an Imperial Mathematician in the court of the holy Roman Emperor, Tycho Brahen, invited Johannes Kepler to join him in Prague.

Johannes Kepler accepted the invitation and travelled to Prague with the hopes of completing his research about the movement of the planets

The journey to Prague is difficult as well as Johannes Kepler's marriage. His wife did not understand his profession and, so he described her as melancholy, stupid, lonely and sulking.

He became a colleague of the infamous mathematician Tycho Brahe. However, being a potential rival is a bit pretentious,

Johannes Kepler was not given a chance to observe with Tycho Brahe.

As Tycho dies to a urinary tract infection however, all of his observations were given to his rival Johannes Kepler. Johannes Kepler replaced Tycho Brahe as the new imperial mathematician and thus continued Tycho Brahe's discovery.

Various observations and records show utter disagreement with Johanne Kepler's Cosmic mystery. Observations of planetary movement show absolutely no connections with the platonic solids, as well as the position of the planets.

After some time, Kepler discovered and theorized the exact movement of the planets around the sun. With improvements and more evidences, it is almost as near as it is right now in the modern age.

The lifelong quest of Johannes Kepler to understand the motions of planets culminated thirty-six years after his death, with the work of Isaac Newton. Newton is known as the greatest scientific genius who have ever lived.

Newton discovered plenty of things such as the Law of Inertia, integral calculus, gravity, and so much more.

His prodigious intellectual prowess stands unmatched by various rivals. His discoveries further strengthened the theories of Johannes Kepler. They both represent a critical period in human history, new discoveries sprung forth from their research. Just like Ptolemy and Kepler, he is modest before his dying breath. He wrote: "do not know what I may appear to the world; but to myself I seem to have been only like a boy, playing on the seashore, and diverting myself, in now and then finding a smoother pebble or a prettier shell than ordinary, while the great ocean of truth lay all undiscovered before me."

The thing is, understanding and exploring the cosmos helped in uniting various people for the greater good of mankind.

Chapter 4: Heaven and Hell

The doors of heaven and hell are adjacent and identical.

—Nikos Kazantzakis, *The Last Temptation of Christ*

The Earth is lovely and beautiful, well, it is our home. It is a placid place but it is also the meeting place of various disaster occurring phenomena.

The Earth helped lifeforms to survive, she gave them food to eat, water to drink, and air to breath – all are the necessary things for survival. In our home, we will find all the tools needed for survival but in also our home, we will also meet our demise.

Many disaster occurring phenomena have already claimed countless umber of lives all throughout the age of our mother Earth. These disasters helped in the evolution of various species through the method of forced death. These disasters changed the environment, killed the current inhabitants of an era and awoke new lifeforms. These lifeforms will then inhabit the newly refreshed surface of the Earth until the time comes that another great disaster will happen again.

Such disasters are meteor strikes. Meteors are just comets

that have entered our atmosphere and is now on its way to create a large crater on the Earth's surface.

A comet will become a meteor upon passing the Earth's atmosphere. The Earth's gravity will pull the meteor towards the Earth, thus crashing onwards our home.

In recent times, discovering a crater is very rare because of various variables taking place. In time, craters will be healed and covered naturally by erosion and weathering. That is why there are a number of various craters on the moon, our home's own satellite because the moon has no atmosphere, no winds to trigger weathering and erosion.

Research and studies suggest that craters on the moon are caused by plenty of meteorite impacts millions or even billions of years ago. The birth of the moon is also said to be caused by a large scale disastrous meteorite impact on our planet. The debris caused by this disastrous event is said to have compacted until it is like the moon that we see today.

Craters are also found in other planets such as Mars, Mercury, and Venus. Just like on our planet Earth and on the moon, these craters are caused by meteorite strikes from a long time ago.

There is one speculation however, that the planet Venus is also a habitable planet. Scientists long time ago speculated that comets have water stored within them. This water will be then transferred to the planet they will crash upon, providing the planet with water.

Venus is said to be habitable with this theory. A number of meteor strikes would mean an increasing amount of water was being supplied to the Planet Venus. Also, its distance to the sun is about the same as planet Earth so why not speculate?

The thing is however, that Venus is full of greenhouse gases. These greenhouse gases prevent the Sun's rays to reflect towards to space. Instead, the planet's atmosphere traps these rays within it not reflecting it, thus, making Venus even hotter and hotter as time goes by.

Comets and meteorite shards are speculated to come from the asteroid belt and from the rings of Saturn, Jupiter, and Uranus. A shard or debris will be pulled by the gravity of other planets, towards the sun until it will become a comet to strike down any unlucky planet or celestial object.

With Venus and Mars being proven to be inhabitable by various reasons, we are safe to say that Earth is our only home. However, we humans, as intelligent as we are, continuously destroys our own home through various methods such as burning fossil fuels, burning forests for wood, using coal, using products that emit carbon dioxide, and polluting bodies of water. The time will come that greenhouse gases will increase and planet Earth will become like the planet Venus.

Cherish our planet, for which it is small and weak but enough for us to thrive upon. Protect our fragile world, for the future generations and for the mankind to prosper and explore the cosmos.

Chapter 5: Blues for a Red Planet

In the orchards of the gods, he watches the canals ...

—*Enuma Elish*, Sumer, c. 2500 B.C.

A man that is of Copernicus' Opinion, that this Earth of ours is a Planet, carry'd round and enlightn'd by the Sun, like the rest of them, cannot but sometimes have a fancy ... that the rest of the Planets have their Dress and Furniture, nay and their Inhabitants too as well as

this Earth of ours.... But we were always apt to conclude, that 'twas in vain to enquire after what Nature had been pleased to do there, seeing there was no likelihood of ever coming to an end of the Enquiry ... but a while ago, thinking somewhat seriously on this

matter (not that I count my self quicker sighted than those great Men [of the past], but that I had the happiness to live after most of them) me thoughts the Enquiry was not so impracticable nor the way so stopt up with Difficulties, but that there was very good room left for probable Conjectures.

—Christiaan Huygens, New Conjectures *Concerning the*

Planetary Worlds, Their Inhabitants and Productions,

c. 1690

Many years ago, we have set out eyes upon Mars, on whether there is life on it. Repeated searches for preliminary lifeforms in Mars called Martians has been unsuccessful and thus being called as, ambiguous by various individuals.

Mars is very earthlike at a first glance, which is why most astronomers first deduced that there is life on Mars because of having similar characteristics with our planet Earth.

Various people helped in exploring Mars through various instruments: Percival Lowell, founded a major observatory to help observe Mars, Giovanni Schiaparelli observed canals on Mars, and Alfred Russel Wallace who critiqued Percival Lowell's work.

As a child, I have also read many works about Martians, there are different interpretations of these lifeforms in various literary works.

A great feat for exploring our neighborhood is the rocket. Robert Goddard first developed a rocket capable of high altitude flight, possibly where our modern rockets are based upon.

Early applications for the space rocket was to be able to launch an orbiting scientific station to monitor Earth from a great height and possible even to probe for Mars.

Me and my colleagues has made various experiments were made to test whether lifeforms can survive in Mars. Most microbes have not survived however, there is a variant of terrestrial microbe that can survive. If terrestrial microbes can somehow survive and grow, what more if there is a Mars microbe?

Till now, the Soviet Union maintains an active program of unmanned planetary exploration. There exploration helped in discovering our neighborhood.

The Soviet Union first started a program for unmanned planetary exploration, next is the NASA. Both of these entities helped in discovering the harsh environment of Mars as well as its Terrain.

Some of Soviet Union's spacecrafts that helped in taking visible photographs of Mars are the Mars 1-7 spacecrafts. NASA's spacecrafts, the Mariner 8 and Viking 1 and 2, have taken more visible photographs than the Soviet Union's spacecrafts.

Most biologist of that time has no instrument capable of looking for microorganisms so Wolf Vishniac, an American microbiologist, developed a small device called the Wolf trap to test the microorganisms on Mars.

Despite having limited budget, Wolf Vishniac never yield. All of his researches, have made significant contributions to modern Science. He made voyages to Antarctica, because Antarctica has similarities to Mars' terrain.

Harold Morowitz had calculated what it would cost to put together all the molecular constituents that make up the human body, it is about ten million dollars.

Till now, presence of lifeforms in Mars is very vague. If the planet ever is terraformed, it will be done by beings whose permanent affiliation and permanent residence is with Mars. Well, the Martians could be us in the near future.

Chapter 6: Traveler's Tales

Do there exist many worlds, or is there but a single world? This is one of the most noble and exalted questions in the study of Nature.

—Albertus Magnus, thirteenth century

We may mount from this dull Earth, and viewing it from on high, consider whether Nature has laid out all her cost and finery upon this small speck of Dirt. So, like Travellers into other distant countries, we shall be better able to judge of what's done at home, know how to make a true estimate of, and set its own value upon every thing. We shall be less apt to admire what this World calls great, shall nobly despise those Trifles the generality of Men set their Affections on, when we know that there are a multitude of such Earths inhabited and adorn'd as well as our own.

—Christiaan Huygens,

The Celestial Worlds Discovered, c. 1690

This is now the time when humans have begun to sail the sea of space, to sail the sea of cosmos even for just a short distance. Voyages to the outer solar system are only controlled from a single place on the planet Earth. This place is the Jet Propulsion Laboratory (JPL) of the National Aeronautics and Space Administration (NASA) located in Pasadena, California.

On the year 1979 in the month of July, Voyager 2 have encountered the Jupiter System. For over 2 years, it had finally reached Jupiter. It is powered by a small nuclear plant using a pellet of Plutonium.

Jupiter's atmosphere is made up off high-energy charged particles, it is also surrounded by a ring of solid debris for which a collision would result in disaster. With the efforts of human intelligence however, Voyager 2 successfully reached Jupiter.

This is likened to the way humans sailed the oceans of this world. At first, it takes a few months to traverse the Atlantic Ocean and America but now, it only takes a few hours. Transportation has never been so easier through technology, just give it time to be improved and in no time, we might sail the cosmos at a much faster pace.

Several entities such as the Dutch East Asia Company contributed to the discoveries of many lands because these entities sent ships all around the globe to find goods and resell them in order to gain profit. Another example is the

Amsterdam Town hall, it represents the confidence of Holland and sent shiploads of Marble of construction to several places in the Globe to assist in development of communities especially in the 17th century.

In the year 1615, a known Italian Scientist named Galileo has close ties to Holland and was being threatened by the Roman Catholic Church for proposing and providing evidence that the Sun is the center of the solar system. He had been offered a professorship by the University of Leiden. Just like Tycho Brahe, Johannes Kepler, and Nicholas Copernicus, he stated that the Earth moves around the sun and not Vice Versa. He does not claimed it as possible, he claimed it as a fact.

There are many notable people in Italy that are interested in Astronomy and Astrology as well. Galileo Galilei, Giordano Bruno, Christiaan Huygens, are only some of these people. They speculated about other worlds and other lifeforms in the Cosmos.

Inventions were prized in that era for which development is necessary for humans to prosper. A prized example is the Leeuwenhoek's microscope that has evolved from magnifying glasses to a more modern microscope. Christiaan Huygens helped Leeuwenhoek to make this microscope.

Both the telescope and microscope were developed during

the early seventeenth century Holland, representing the human intelligence and vision to explore the realms of space.

Huygens also speculated that if our star has planets surrounding it with a single inhabitable planet for lifeforms to exist, are there also lifeforms in other stars? The universe is so vast that the probability is high.

The voyager spacecraft may be a descendant of those ships that helped explore our world. These spacecrafts are on their way to discover new things in the Cosmic Ocean.

Jupiter's satellites are as large as Mercury. Unlike other satellites such as our moon, these satellites are significantly larger.

The Voyager 2, a spacecraft that has reached Jupiter sent a picture of its Satellite named Europa.

Pictures in space are taken due to the Sun's light reflecting off of the celestial bodies.

If the voyager system were manned, and a captain will take logs, it will be something just like this:

Day 1: We have successfully lifted from the Cape Canaveral albeit with difficulties.

Day 2: There is a problem with the deployment of the boom, it needs to be fixed as soon as possible.

Day 13: We have taken pictures of the Earth and the Moon.

Day 150: Engines fired for a trajectory correction.

Day 170: Housekeeping.

Day 185: Images of Jupiter.

Day 207: Boom problem solved but the main transmitter malfunctioned, back-up transmitter is used.

Day 215: Crossed the orbit of Mars.

Day 295: Entered the Asteroid Belt.

Day 475: Survived from the Asteroid Belt.

Day 570: Jupiter can now be seen more clearly.

Day 615: Jupiter is...made of gas, clouds, and storm.

Day 630: The weather on Jupiter is very wild and spontaneous.

Day 640: The cloud patterns on Jupiter are so lovely and beautiful.

Day 647: The great red spot. So large and so old.

Day 650: A day of wanders, a day of beauty and success.

Day 662: Left Jupiter.

Day 874: Onward to the Saturn system.

Jupiter is a large hulking beautiful planet, it has no surface, just gases, clouds, and constant storms. It is a beauty with a harsh personality.

We have already embarked on epic voyages indeed.

Chapter 7: The Backbone of Night

I would rather understand one cause than be King of Persia.

—Democritus of Abdera

If a faithful account was rendered of Man's ideas upon Divinity, he would be obliged to acknowledge, that for the most part the word "gods" has been used to express the concealed, remote, unknown causes of the effects he witnessed; that he applies this term

when the spring of the natural, the source of known causes, ceases to be visible: as soon as he loses the thread of these causes, or as soon as his mind can no longer follow the chain, he solves the difficulty, terminates his research, by ascribing it to his gods ... When, therefore, he ascribes to his gods the production of some phenomenon ... does he, in fact, do any thing more than substitute for the darkness of his own mind, a sound to which he has been accustomed to listen with reverential awe?

—Paul Heinrich Dietrich, Baron von Holbach,

Système de la Nature, London, 1770

When I was a child, I lived in the Bensonhurst section of

116

Brooklyn in the City of New York. I knew my neighborhood perfectly, with fine detail if I must say.

Even in early bedtime, in Winter you could sometimes see the stars. I wonder what they are, I asked many people, young and old alike, they all say the same thing, "They are lights in the sky kid". Well yes, I know that they are lights in the sky but just what they are? What are they made off? What do they look like when we are near to them? Curiosity compels my mind to wonder, what is beyond the darkness of the night? Is this darkness eternal? With no end to it? Is there light in this darkness?

When I was old enough, my parents gave me a library card, my first library card. I asked the librarian for something about the stars and she gave me one, it was about Clark Gable and Jean Harlow. Who the hell are they? I asked for another one, and alas, it is the right one. I marveled, it is said that stars are just faraway suns in the cosmos.

The book also mentioned that the Earth revolves around the sun. Well an astonishing fact indeed. I ask about stars however, just what are those things? What are those lights that I look upon in the night sky?

Sometimes in my fantasies, I imagine that there is someone who thought like this:

Are stars like campfires? What if stars are just a huge fireball up in the sky? Like these are the thoughts a hunter in the forest during night time.

Or what if the stars are just holes in a giant black animal skin up in the sky? And in those holes, we see flame burning brightly within the animal's body.

These ideas were eventually replaced by another mortal idea, those celestial beings were promoted to be Gods themselves watching over us mortals.

Our ancestors believe, well till now, that everything in this world is created by a supreme being, by Gods and Goddesses. Especially in ancient Greek and Rome, their Gods are the manifestations of their own environment and elements. For example, the Greek God of thunder, Zeus. He is the strongest Greek God there is for which he is the king of the Gods. The God of the sun, Helios, the god of war, Ares. All these gods are their manifestation of various elements in the world.

For thousands of years, we humans have failed to comprehend the fundamental components of our universe's existence. We used to believe and worship Gods believing that everything in this world is created by them, to know the purpose of our existence. To know why we are here in this world, what is our goal?

Until suddenly, people believed that everything in this world is made of atoms; not just this world, even the universe is made up of atoms. These brilliant people came from Ionia, but why Ionia out of many more well-known developed countries?

Ionia have several advantages, they have diversity among their people, they have the freedom to express their thoughts without a single hive mind controlling their ideals. The freedom of expression is really helpful to cultivate brilliant minds, to free their wisdom, not to contain it.

These visionaries in Ionia are: Thales of Miletus, Anaximander, Theodoros of Samos, Democritus, Aristotle, and Pythagoras. They all helped in giving more knowledge for science and wisdom for our existence.

We all lingered within the shores of the cosmic ocean, we are wanderers, and we are wanderers still. We are ready to embark even more further towards the Cosmic Ocean.

Chapter 8: Travels in Space and Time

We have loved the stars too fondly to be fearful of the night.

—Tombstone epitaph of two amateur astronomers

Stars are balls of gas with an unlimited supply of fuel to keep it burning for ages. They provide light for the universe, without stars, the universe is an eternal dark.

Drawings in the sky are called constellations, group of stars that are aligned to show a certain pattern or shape, or even an object. The patterns of constellations are constant throughout any part of the world. No matter where you are, the big dipper will always look the same way it used to be.

Constellations are also constantly changing. At ancient times, constellations are quite different, for example, the big dipper used to look like a spear when compared to the current big dipper. It is long and pointy at the tip.

The stars in the constellations constantly give off light throughout the space. As we all know, light travels at 1 billion km/hr in a vacuum. This fixed speed helps us in calculating the distance of other stars and galaxies.

One of the methods used to calculating the distance of other celestial bodies is called "standard candle." Standard candles are repetitive explosions that emit the same amount of light throughout the cosmos. We calculate the distance by comparing the amount of light observed here on Earth to the actual amount of brightness which is known.

Knowing if whether or not an object or a celestial body is moving is done through identifying the blueshift or redshift phenomena. Blue shifting celestial bodies are moving towards us while red shifting objects are moving away from us. We have also discovered that most of the celestial bodies and objects in space are red shifting, moving away from us. Their speed is also not constant, it is on an accelerating rate. This means that the universe is still constantly expanding faster and faster every second.

Another fact about light is that the moment that a light from a faraway object reaches us, it is already travelling for a very long time, considering the vastness of the cosmos. This means that if we have seen an explosion in space, it has happened millions of years ago, but its light is just reaching our planet. This phenomenon is called "quasars" but such quasars may be already not in a state to classify them as such. Years have passed since light left such objects and celestial bodies, they can be even called as "ghosts".

We may never reach a quasar but someday, maybe a million

years from now, we can. With our current technology, we can only do enough for our future descendants to continue our work, improving current research to greater heights.

Chapter 9: The Lives of the Stars

We had the sky, up there, all speckled with stars, and we used to lay on our backs and look up at them, and discuss about whether they were made, or only just happened.

—Mark Twain, *Huckleberry Finn*

I have ... a terrible need ... shall I say the word? ... of religion. Then I go out at night and paint the stars.

—Vincent van Gogh

Knowing the limits and fundamentals are probably some of the best ways to understand a phenomenon. We have known that everything in this world is made up of tiny particles called atoms. These atoms are said to be so small that we can fit a hundred million of them on the tip of our middle finger. And as new technological developments advanced, we discovered that these tiny particles are even made up of much smaller particles: the nucleus, proton, and electron. The nucleus of an atom is the last particle discovered because of its size which is really small compared to other particles in the atom, making it really hard to recognize or even see the nucleus. Luckily, technological advancements enable us to see the nucleus.

Electrical charges in the atom is also the reason behind why we are not going through other objects. Technically, matter is made up of nothing because an atom is just made up of particles and electrical charges. These electrical charges are the defining factor of compound structures. Without these electrical charges, our whole environment would be nothing but a messy cloud of particles.

Enough with these small things, we humans have made significant discoveries with the stars. Observing stars has given us humans insight on how does matter assembles and transforms to another form. All throughout history, we also found parallel discoveries with the stars and atoms. An example is the helium gas, it was discovered in the sun before it was found here in Earth, hence the name stemming from the Greek God of the sun, Helios.

Observing the stars gave us the information needed to understand their life cycles. The pressure inside the star is so dense that the hydrogen particles are forced to fuse, forming a bigger atom. This is called nuclear fusion, it releases light and heat. This is why stars are so bright, because of nuclear fusion. Our sun is a small star fusing hydrogen atom to form larger helium atoms.

The sun will eventually run out of fuel however, opting to fuse helium instead to form larger atoms. When that happens, the sun will now enter the last phase of a star's life cycle, death. It will enter a long and agonizing series of events leading to its death. The first of these events is the migration of the fusion reaction towards to surface of the sun, until gravity pulls it back together to perform helium fusion.

Larger stars can do the fusion "step-up" more than once as they are dying, but our sun is just small, so it could only step-up once, to helium fusion. The sun will expand as soon as it has step-upped to helium fusion, possibly reaching the Earth as it becomes a red giant.

Red giants are very unstable, with million tons of stellar dust constantly being shed into space by our sun. When enough stellar dust has been shed by our sun, our sun will shrink, becoming a red dwarf with plenty of planetary nebula surrounding it.

When there is not enough mass to sustain all the fusion, it will just stop. The sun will cool for a very long time, becoming a white dwarf. And when it has become cold enough, the sun will become a black dwarf, a sad black dwarf.

In binary systems however (binary systems are two stars close to each other, with the other star being smaller than the other star), they have different fate than our lonely star.

It is highly likely that the other star will become a white dwarf before the other star. When the white dwarf is next to a red giant, its gravity will attract the red giant's stellar dust. This exchange of gases triggers Novae, a series of explosions until they both cool, becoming white dwarfs and then black dwarfs.

Bigger stars have a different death as well, they contract and then explode vividly, also known as a supernova. A supernova releases a bunch of heavy elements into the cosmos in just a matter of seconds and then the star will become brighter than its entire home galaxy.

A huge nebula will be left behind by this event, but also, there will be a collection of neutrons at the center of the explosion. These entity is called a neutron star. Neutron stars are rotating rapidly and they all produce some of the highest magnetic fields ever detected. Neutron stars don't emit much visible light and they are the heaviest stars.

The nebula from a supernova explosion has heavy elements. Some areas in the nebulae may still have enough mass to create smaller stars and celestial bodies. These heavy elements produced during the explosion are almost the same as the heavy elements found on Earth, so we are also made from star stuff.

Stars that are much larger than supernova stars explode at a much greater energy, these explosions are called hypernovae.

After the explosion, these stars become so dense that even light cannot escape them, also known as black holes.

We are all connected to the cosmos, our very own character has connections with life and the cosmos.

Chapter 10: The Edge of Forever

There is a way on high, conspicuous in the clear heavens, called the Milky Way, brilliant with its own brightness. By it the gods go to the dwelling of the great Thunderer and his royal abode ... Here the famous and mighty inhabitants of heaven have their homes. This

is the region which I might make bold to call the Palatine [Way] of the Great Sky.

—Ovid, *Metamorphoses* (Rome, first century)

Some foolish men declare that a Creator made the world. The doctrine that the world was created is ill-advised, and should be rejected.

If God created the world, where was He before creation? ... How could God have made the world without any raw material? If you say He made this first, and then the world, you are faced with an endless regression ... Know that the world is uncreated, as time itself is,

without beginning and end. And it is based on the principles ...

—The Mahapurana (The Great Legend),

Jinasena (India, ninth century)

The universe is already 13.9 billion years old. Thanks to the much-limited speed of light, we can identify and come into the conclusion that the universe is constantly expanding. Hundreds of millions of years ago, we can conclude that the universe is much hotter and much brighter than it is at the present time.

The universe is also smaller billion years ago than it is right now, due to the fact that it is constantly expanding throughout all those years.

One of the evidences to support this fact is the way quasars look. Quasars are really far from us, the closest one is about 2.3 billion light years away from us, which is pretty huge when compared to the Andromeda galaxy which is only around 2.5 million light years away. These quasars are still so bright, that their estimated actual brightness is close to a thousand supernovas exploding in unison. Scientists suggests that galaxies are caused by the explosion of these quasars. Just like the big bang, the explosion of quasars will cause different materials to be invoked in the cosmos, these materials will form different celestial bodies such as stars, planets, satellites, nebula, and other celestial bodies.

This further supported the claim that at first, there was

nothing, until the big bang happened. The big bang is an explosion so huge that it created the universe out of nothing. It is the reason why we are living right now. The big bang causes different materials to be created thus, forming different celestial bodies in a larger scale compared to quasars.

Speculations about the universe being from nothingness is evident even from the old ancient times. Even the big bang theory has an ancient predecessor speculated by philosophers and prophets alike.

The universe is ever expanding, with no limits, it has no definite edge, the only thing that is limited is our understanding of the cosmos itself. We need to remove this edge, smoothen it first and then remove it in order to also expand our knowledge about the cosmos.

Chapter 11: The Persistence of Memory

Now that the destinies of Heaven and Earth have been fixed;

Trench and canal have been given their proper course;

The banks of the Tigris and the Euphrates

have been established;

What else shall we do?

What else shall we create?

Oh Anunaki, you great gods of the sky,

what else shall we do?

—The Assyrian account of the creation of Man, 800 B.C.

How did we come to be? Are we alone?

These questions are the only way to justify our existence, we are curious and intelligent beings, are there other lifeforms like us in the cosmos? Just how did we come to be? Is there someone in the sky engineering our bodies?

Our DNA contains the genetic code needed to engineer a lifeform's body, it identifies what type of lifeform will be brought to life, its characteristics, intelligence, and its traits.

The DNA helped us to be as complex as we are today. Our DNA is the blueprint of our existence.

Reproduction is the reason that every lifeform is still existing. Given the correct time and environment, having an offspring is the key to a species' survival such as us humans. Replication is not perfect however, because there are cases that small errors can occur and will affect the offspring. Radiation and even the simplest replication mistakes causes this error. These errors are called mutation, and believe it or not, these mutations are the driving force of evolution. These replication mistakes made every single organism on Earth.

An evidence of evolution is our brain, the r-complex, which is also called the reptilian brain is responsible for our instincts. It is called the reptilian brain because reptiles also have similar brain structures, and they act on instinct. Surrounding the reptilian brain is the limbic system, or the mammalian brain. The mammalian brain is responsible for our moods and emotions. Surrounding all of these is the cerebral cortex which is only found on some mammals.

The DNA contains lots of information including the behavior of animals for example, wolves know how to walk and run from the day they were born, they know how to drink milk and whine. They don't know where to hunt however, because such information is learned by various circumstances.

This information learned by various circumstances cannot be replicated through reproduction, the information is taught instead by the parents or the society surrounding the offspring. The cerebral cortex can overtake the instinctive way of thinking of our reptilian brain, replacing it with moral values instead.

Information is also absorbed through literacy, writing is probably one of the greatest inventions of humans. It is a great way to pass down information to other generations, just like the DNA, passing down information from generation to generations.

The time will come when we humans have found a way to replicate information down to the last detail in order for the future generations to learn from it.

Such time is only a dream however, as long as people around the Earth is not unified and accomplishing a common goal: to cherish life and be a communing figure for galactic societies.

Chapter 12: Encyclopedia Galactica

"What are you? From where did you come? I have never seen anything like you." The -Creator Raven looked at Man and was ... surprised to find that this strange new being was

so much like himself.

—An Eskimo creation myth

The author of Nature ... has made it impossible for us to have any communication from this earth with the other great bodies of the universe, in our present state; and it is highly possible that he has likewise cut off all communication betwixt the other planets, and

betwixt the different systems.... We observe, in all of them, enough to raise our curiosity, but not to satisfy it ... It does not appear to be suitable to the wisdom that shines throughout all nature, to suppose that we should see so far, and have our curiosity so much raised ... only to be disappointed at the end ... This, therefore, naturally leads us to consider our present state as only the dawn or beginning of our existence, and as a state of preparation or probation for farther advancement....

The probability of us being alone in the universe is very slim. But at the same time, there are no evidences to support the claim that there are indeed other intelligent lifeforms out there, not just us. Just, where are they?

The infamous Fermi paradox, named after the physicist Enrico Fermi, is the contradiction between high probability estimates and lack of evidence to prove the existence of other intelligent lifeforms.

It is made by physicists Enrico Fermi and Michael Hart; its basic points of argument are:

- There are plenty of stars in the Galaxy that are similar to our Sun, and these stars are older than our sun's solar system.

- Some of these stars have Earth-like planets, with a high probability that these planets have developed intelligent lifeforms.

- Some alien civilizations may have access to interstellar travel, which is something that our scientists are currently investigating.

- The Milky Way Galaxy can be traversed completely in a few million years.

With these reasons, extraterrestrial lifeforms should have visited Earth a long time ago, but where is everybody?

The infamous question, where is everybody? Was exclaimed by Enrico Fermi during a conversation with his colleagues Emil Konopinski, Edward Teller, and Herbert York.

Explaining the Fermi paradox is difficult, either suggesting that intelligent lifeforms are rare or that such civilizations have yet to contact Earth.

The time will come that a galactic federation will be formed, uniting various intelligent lifeforms for the improvement of the universe. Different literary works such as star trek and Star Wars are close enough in depicting the future of cosmic lifeforms with us being somewhat of a communing figure.

The thing is, we are not alone in this universe, various discoveries and hypotheses have shown that the probability of us being alone in this universe is really small. The time will come where we will find intelligent life elsewhere, or we will be contacted by them.

Being alone is hard, having someone is a great help for improvement. Having another lifeform to communicate to is great for the overall improvement of our species.

Chapter 13: Who Speaks for Earth?

To what purpose should I trouble myself in searching out the secrets of the stars, having death or slavery continually before my eyes?

—A question put to Pythagoras by Anaximenes (c. 600 B.C.),

according to Montaigne

How vast those Orbs must be, and how inconsiderable this Earth, the Theatre upon which all our mighty Designs, all our Navigations, and all our Wars are transacted, is when compared to them. A very fit consideration, and matter of Reflection, for those Kings and

Princes who sacrifice the Lives of so many People, only to flatter their Ambition in being Masters of some pitiful corner of this small Spot.

—Christiaan Huygens, *New Conjectures Concerning the Planetary*

Worlds, Their Inhabitants and Productions, c. 1690

The human species has been around for about 200,000 years, and we have only proved our intelligence recently, around 1000 years ago. We owe our knowledge to science, even the advancement of our specie is because of science. It is said that science was invented during the Ionian awakening, however, it was delayed due to religion and slavery. Our curiosity proved to be the main reason behind all our discoveries and exploration. Our curiosity is also one of the reasons why our species is prone to chaotic activities and outcomes.

Curiosity is good until it becomes too much, where there will be negative outcomes. An example is a child's curiosity, it may be innocent, but a child lacks complete understanding of various fundamentals and values.

We have invented a lot of things throughout the years of human development. New inventions also invite new questions to be answered by us. New questions to be answered by science and research using our intelligence and wisdom to prove answers with factual information.

The thing is, we humans are chaotic beings, we have the power to unleash destruction upon ourselves. If we will not care enough, we will be the reason for our own extinction. We need to care for our own species for future generations to come for these generations will continue our work and research about the cosmos.

Humans are good at surviving because of the presence of the mammalian brain, it conflicts with our reptilian brain however, thus creating various emotional issues. And conflicting with our own moral choices.

This reptilian brain acts purely on instincts, and when stimulated enough, it can cause violent reactions on the society – such things are even recorded throughout our history such as aggressiveness.

We are aware of ourselves, so why not be aware at everything around us? Pay attention to the things that will help unite different people, regardless of barriers such as nationality, social statues, ethnicity, etc.

We are beings of the cosmos that have developed self-awareness, contemplating our origins and about everything in this universe. We are loyal to our planet, to our species...we speak for the Earth itself. We need to survive, for we are the greatest creation of the cosmos so far.

Acknowledgments

I am very grateful to the many people who generously contributed their time and expertise to this book, including Carol Lane, Myrna Talman, and Jenny Arden; David Oyster, Richard Wells, Tom Weidlinger, Dennis Gutierrez, Rob McCain, Nancy Kinney, Janelle Balnicke, Judy Flannery, and Susan Racho of the *Cosmos* television staff; Nancy Inglis, Peter Mollman, Marylea O'Reilly, and Jennifer Peters of Random House; Paul west for generously lending me the title of Chapter 5; and George Abell, James Allen, Barbara Amago, Lawrence Anderson, Jonathon Arons, Halton Arp, Asma El Bakri, James Blinn, Bart Bok, Zeddie Bowen, John C. Brandt, Kenneth Brecher, Frank Bristow, John Callendar, Donald B. Campbell, Judith Campbell, Elof Axel Carlson, Michael Carra, John Cassani, Judith Castagno, Catherine Cesarsky, Martin Cohen, Judy-Lynn del Rey, Nicholas Devereux, Michael Devirian, Stephen Dole, Frank D. Drake, Frederick C. Durant III, Richard Epstein, Von R. Eshleman, Ahmed

Fahmy, Herbert Friedman, Robert Frosch, Jon Fukuda, Richard

Gammon, Ricardo Giacconi, Thomas Gold, Paul

Goldenberg, Peter Goldreich, Paul Goldsmith, J. Richard Gott III, Stephen Jay Gould, Bruce Hayes, Raymond Heacock, Wulff Heintz, Arthur Hoag, Paul Hodge, Dorrit Hoffleit, William Hoyt, Icko Iben, Mikhail Jaroszynski, Paul Jepsen, Tom Karp, Bishun N. Khare, Charles Kohlhase, Edwin Krupp, Arthur Lane, Paul MacLean, Bruce Margon, Harold Masursky, Linda Morabito, Edmond Momjian, Edward Moreno, Bruce Murray, William Murnane, Thomas A. Mutch, Kenneth Norris, Tobias Owen, Linda Paul, Roger Payne, Vahe Petrosian, James B. Pollack, George Preston, Nancy Priest, Boris Ragent, Dianne Rennell, Michael Rowton, Allan Sandage, Fred Scarf, Maarten Schmidt, Arnold Scheibel, Eugene Shoemaker, Frank Shu, Nathan Sivin, Bradford Smith, Laurence A. Soderblom, Hyron Spinrad, Edward Stone, Jeremy Stone, Ed Taylor, Kip S. Thorne, Norman Thrower, O. Brian Toon, Barbara Tuchman, Roger Ulrich, Richard Underwood, Peter van de Kamp, Jurrie J. Van der Woude, Arthur Vaughn, Joseph Veverka, Helen Simpson Vishniac, Dorothy Vitaliano, Robert Wagoner, Pete Waller, Josephine Walsh, Kent Weeks, Donald Yeomans, Stephen Yerazunis, Louise Gray Young, Harold Zirin, and the National Aeronautics and Space Administration. I am also grateful for special photographic help by Edwardo Castañeda and Bill Ray.

For Further Reading

CHAPTER 1

Boeke, Kees. *Cosmic View: The Universe in Forty Jumps*. New York: John Day, 1957.

Fraser, Peter Marshall. *Ptolemaic Alexandria*. Three volumes. Oxford: Clarendon Press, 1972.

Morison, Samuel Eliot. *Admiral of the Ocean Sea: A Life of Christopher Columbus*. Boston: Little,

Brown, 1942.

Sagan, Carl. *Broca's Brain: Reflections on the Romance of Science*. New York: Random House,

1979.

CHAPTER 2

Attenborough, David. *Life on Earth: A Natural History*. London: British Broadcasting Corporation,

1979.

*Dobzhansky, Theodosius, Ayala, Francisco J., Stebbins, G. Ledyard and Valentine, James.

Evolution. San Francisco: W.H. Freeman, 1978.

Evolution. A Scientific American Book. San Francisco: W.H. Freeman, 1978.

Gould, Stephen Jay. *Ever Since Darwin: Reflections on Natural History*. New York: W.W. Norton,

1977.

Handler, Philip (ed.). *Biology and the Future of Man*. Committee on Science and Public Policy,

National Academy of Sciences. New York: Oxford University Press, 1970.

Huxley, Julian. *New Bottles for New Wine: Essays*. London: Chatto and Windus, 1957.

Kennedy, D. (ed.). *Cellular and Organismal Biology*. A Scientific American Book. San Francisco:

W.H. Freeman, 1974.

*Kornberg, A. *DNA Replication*. San Francisco: W.H. Freeman, 1980.

*Miller, S.L. and Orgel, L. *The Origins of Life on Earth*. Englewood Cliffs, N.J.: Prentice-Hall,

1974.

Orgel, L. *Origins of Life*. New York: Wiley, 1973.

*Roemer, A.S. "Major Steps in Vertebrate Evolution." *Science*, Vol. 158, p. 1629, 1967.

*Roland, Jean Claude. *Atlas of Cell Biology*. Boston: Little, Brown, 1977.

Sagan, Carl. "Life." *Encyclopaedia Britannica*, 1970 and later printings.

*Sagan, Carl and Salpeter, E.E. "Particles, Environments and Hypothetical Ecologies in the

Jovian Atmosphere." *Astrophysical Journal Supplement*, Vol. 32, p. 737, 1976.

Simpson, G.G. *The Meaning of Evolution*. New Haven: Yale University Press, 1960.

Thomas, Lewis. *Lives of a Cell: Notes of a Biology Watcher*. New York: Bantam Books, 1974.

*Watson, J.D. *Molecular Biology of the Gene*. New York: W.A. Benjamin, 1965.

Wilson, E.O., Eisner, T., Briggs, W.R., Dickerson, R.E., Metzenberg, R.L., O'Brien, R.D., Susman,

M., and Boggs, W.E. *Life on Earth*. Stamford: Sinauer Associates, 1973.

CHAPTER 3

Abell, George and Singer, B. (eds.) *Science and the Paranormal.* New York: Scribner's, 1980.

*Beer, A. (ed.). *Vistas in Astronomy: Kepler*, Vol. 18. London: Pergamon Press, 1975.

Caspar, Max. *Kepler.* London: Abelard-Schuman, 1959.

Cumont, Franz. *Astrology and Religion Among the Greeks and Romans.* New York: Dover, 1960.

Koestler, Arthur. *The Sleepwalkers.* New York: Grosset and Dunlap, 1963.

Krupp, E.C. (ed.). *In Search of Ancient Astronomies.* New York: Doubleday, 1978.

Pannekoek, Anton. *A History of Astronomy.* London: George Allen, 1961.

Rey, H.A. *The Stars: A New Way to See Them,* third edition. Boston: Houghton Mifflin, 1970.

Rosen, Edward. *Kepler's Somnium.* Madison, Wis.: University of Wisconsin Press, 1967.

Standen, A. *Forget Your Sun Sign.* Baton Rouge: Legacy, 1977.

Vivian, Gordon and Raiter, Paul. *The Great Kivas of Chaco*

Canyon. Albuquerque: University of

New Mexico Press, 1965.

CHAPTER 4

Chapman, C. *The Inner Planets*. New York: Scribner's, 1977.

Charney, J.G. (ed.). *Carbon Dioxide and Climate: A Scientific Assessment*. Washington, D.C.:

National Academy of Sciences, 1979.

Cross, Charles A. and Moore, Patrick. *The Atlas of Mercury*. New York: Crown Publishers, 1977.

*Delsemme, A.H. (ed.). *Comets, Asteroids, Meteorites*. Toledo: University of Ohio Press, 1977.

Ehrlich, Paul R., Ehrlich, Anne H. and Holden, John P. *Ecoscience: Population, Resources,*

Environment. San Francisco: W.H. Freeman, 1977.

*Dunne, James A. and Burgess, Eric. *The Voyage of Mariner 10*. NASA SP-424. Washington, D.C.:

U.S. Government Printing Office, 1978.

*El-Baz, Farouk. "The Moon After Apollo." *Icarus*, Vol. 25, p. 495, 1975.

Goldsmith, Donald (ed.). *Scientists Confront Velikovsky*. Ithaca: Cornell University Press, 1977.

Kaufmann, William J. *Planets and Moons*. San Francisco: W.H. Freeman, 1979.

*Keldysh, M.V. "Venus Exploration with the Venera 9 and Venera 10 Spacecraft." *Icarus*, Vol.

30, p. 605, 1977.

*Kresak, L. "The Tunguska Object: A Fragment of Comet Encke?" *Bulletin of the Astronomical*

Institute of Czechoslovakia, Vol. 29, p. 129, 1978.

Krinov, E.L. *Giant Meteorites*. New York: Pergamon Press, 1966.

Lovelock, L. *Gaia*. Oxford: Oxford University Press, 1979.

*Marov, M. Ya. "Venus: A Perspective at the Beginning of Planetary Exploration." *Icarus*, Vol.

16, p. 115, 1972.

Masursky, Harold, Colton, C.W. and El-Baz, Farouk (eds.). *Apollo Over the Moon: A View from*

Orbit. NASA SP-362. Washington, D.C.: U.S. Government Printing Office, 1978.

*Mulholland, J.D. and Calame, O. "Lunar Crater Giordano Bruno: AD 1178 Impact Observations

Consistent with Laser Ranging Results." *Science*, Vol. 199, p. 875, 1978.

*Murray, Bruce and Burgess, Eric. *Flight to Mercury*. New York: Columbia University Press, 1977.

*Murray, Bruce, Greeley, R. and Malin, M. *Earthlike Planets*. San Francisco: W.H. Freeman, 1980.

Nicks, Oran W. (ed.). *This Island Earth*. NASA SP250. Washington, D.C.: U.S. Government

Printing Office, 1970.

Oberg, James. "Tunguska: Collision with a Comet." *Astronomy*, Vol. 5, No. 12, p. 18, December

1977.

*Pioneer Venus Results. *Science*, Vol. 203, No. 4382, p. 743, February 23, 1979.

*Pioneer Venus Results. *Science*, Vol. 205, No. 4401, p. 41, July 6, 1979.

Press, Frank and Siever, Raymond. *Earth*, second edition. San Francisco: W.H. Freeman, 1978.

Ryan, Peter and Pesek, L. *Solar System*. New York: Viking, 1979.

*Sagan, Carl, Toon, O.B. and Pollack, J.B. "Anthropogenic Albedo Changes and the Earth's

Climate." *Science*, Vol. 206, p. 1363, 1979.

Short, Nicholas M., Lowman, Paul D., Freden, Stanley C. and Finsh, William A. *Mission to Earth:*

LANDSAT Views the World. NASA SP-360. Washington, D.C.: U.S. Government Printing Office,

1976.

Skylab Explores the Earth. NASA SP-380. Washington, D.C.: U.S. Government Printing Office,

1977.

The Solar System. A Scientific American Book. San Francisco: W.H. Freeman, 1975.

Urey, H.C. "Cometary Collisions in Geological Periods." *Nature*, Vol. 242, p. 32, March 2, 1973.

Vitaliano, Dorothy B. *Legends of the Earth*. Bloomington: Indiana University Press, 1973.

*Whipple, F.L. *Comets*. New York: John Wiley, 1980.

CHAPTER 5

*American Geophysical Union. *Scientific Results of the Viking Project.* Reprinted from the *Journal of Geophysical Research*, Vol. 82, p. 3959, 1977.

Batson, R.M., Bridges, T.M. and Inge, J.L. *Atlas of Mars: The 1:5,000,000 Map Series.* NASA SP-438. Washington, D.C.: U.S. Government Printing Office, 1979.

Bradbury, Ray, Clarke, Arthur C., Murray, Bruce, Sagan, Carl, and Sullivan, Walter. *Mars and the Mind of Man.* New York: Harper and Row, 1973.

Burgess, Eric. *To the Red Planet.* New York: Columbia University Press, 1978.

Gerster, Georg. *Grand Design: The Earth from Above.* New York: Paddington Press, 1976.

Glasstone, Samuel. *Book of Mars.* Washington, D.C.: U.S. Government Printing Office, 1968.

Goddard, Robert H. *Autobiography.* Worcester, Mass.: A.J. St. Onge, 1966.

*Goddard, Robert H. *Papers.* Three volumes. New York: McGraw-Hill, 1970.

Hartmann, W.H. and Raper, O. *The New Mars: The Discoveries of Mariner 9*. NASA SP-337.

Washington, D.C.: U.S. Government Printing Office, 1974.

Hoyt, William G. *Lowell and Mars*. Tucson: University of Arizona Press, 1976.

Lowell, Percival. *Mars*. Boston: Houghton Mifflin, 1896.

Lowell, Percival. *Mars and Its Canals*. New York: Macmillan, 1906.

Lowell, Percival. *Mars as an Abode of Life*. New York: Macmillan, 1908.

Mars as Viewed by Mariner 9. NASA SP-329. Washington, D.C.: U.S. Government Printing Office,

1974.

Morowitz, Harold. *The Wine of Life*. New York: St. Martin's, 1979.

*Mutch, Thomas A., Arvidson, Raymond E., Head, James W., Jones, Kenneth L. and Saunders, R.

Stephen. *The Geology of Mars*. Princeton: Princeton University Press, 1976.

*Pittendrigh, Colin S., Vishniac, Wolf and Pearman, J.P.T. (eds.). *Biology and the Exploration of*

Mars. Washington, D.C.: National Academy of Sciences, National Research Council, 1966.

The Martian Landscape. Viking Lander Imaging Team, NASA SP-425. Washington, D.C.: U.S.

Government Printing Office, 1978.

*Viking 1 Mission Results. *Science*, Vol 193, No. 4255, August 1976.

*Viking 1 Mission Results. *Science*, Vol 194, No. 4260, October 1976.

*Viking 2 Mission Results. *Science*, Vol. 194, No. 4271, December 1976.

*"The Viking Mission and the Question of Life on Mars." *Journal of Molecular Evolution*, Vol. 14, Nos. 1–3. Berlin: Springer-Verlag, December 1979.

Wallace, Alfred Russel. *Is Mars Habitable?* London: Macmillan, 1907.

Washburn, Mark. *Mars At Last!* New York: G.P. Putnam, 1977.

CHAPTER 6

*Alexander, A.F.O. *The Planet Saturn*. New York: Dover, 1980.

Bell, Arthur E. *Christiaan Huygens and the Development of Science in the Seventeenth Century.* New

York: Longman's Green, 1947.

Dobell, Clifford. *Anton Van Leeuwenhoek and His "Little Animals."* New York: Russell and Russell,

1958.

Duyvendak, J.J.L. *China's Discovery of Africa.* London: Probsthain, 1949.

*Gehrels, T. (ed.). *Jupiter: Studies of the Interior, Atmosphere, Magnetosphere and Satellites.* Tucson:

University of Arizona Press, 1976.

Haley, K.H. *The Dutch in the Seventeenth Century.* New York: Harcourt Brace, 1972.

Huizinga, Johan. *Dutch Civilization in the Seventeenth Century.* New York: F. Ungar, 1968.

*Hunten, Donald (ed.). *The Atmosphere of Titan.* NASA SP-340. Washington, D.C.: U.S.

Government Printing Office, 1973.

*Hunten, Donald and Morrison, David (eds.). *The Saturn System.* NASA Conference Publication

2068. Washington, D.C.: U.S. Government Printing Office, 1978.

Huygens, Christiaan. *The Celestial Worlds Discover'd: Conjectures Concerning the Inhabitants,*

Planets and Productions of the Worlds in the Planets. London: Timothy Childs, 1798.

*"First Scientific Results from Voyager 1." *Science*, Vol. 204, No. 4396, June 1, 1979.

*"First Scientific Results from Voyager 2." *Science*, Vol. 206, No. 4421, p. 927, November 23,

1979.

Manuel, Frank E. A *Portrait of Isaac Newton.* Washington: New Republic Books, 1968.

Morrison, David and Samz, Jane. *Voyager to Jupiter.* NASA SP-439. Washington, D.C.: U.S.

Government Printing Office, 1980.

Needham, Joseph. *Science and Civilization in China,* Vol. 4, Part 3, pp. 468–553. New York

Cambridge University Press, 1970.

*Palluconi, F.D. and Pettengill, G.H. (eds.). *The Rings of*

Saturn. NASA SP-343. Washington, D.C.:

U.S. Government Printing Office, 1974.

Rimmel, Richard O., Swindell, William and Burgess, Eric. *Pioneer Odyssey*. NASA SP-349.

Washington, D.C.: U.S. Government Printing Office, 1977.

*"Voyager 1 Encounter with Jupiter and Io." *Nature*, Vol. 280, p. 727, 1979.

Wilson, Charles H. *The Dutch Republic and the Civilization of the Seventeenth Century*. London:

Weidenfeld and Nicolson, 1968.

Zumthor, Paul. *Daily Life in Rembrandt's Holland*. London: Weidenfeld and Nicolson, 1962.

CHAPTER 7

Baker, Howard. *Persephone's Cave*. Athens: University of Georgia Press, 1979.

Berendzen, Richard, Hart, Richard and Seeley, Daniel. *Man Discovers the Galaxies*. New York:

Science History Publications, 1977.

Farrington, Benjamin. *Greek Science*. London: Penguin, 1953.

Finley, M.I. *Ancient Slavery and Modern Ideology*. London: Chatto, 1980.

Frankfort, H., Frankfort, H.A., Wilson, J.A. and Jacobsen, T. *Before Philosophy: The Intellectual*

Adventure of Ancient Man. Chicago: University of Chicago Press, 1946.

Heath, T. *Aristarchus of Samos*. Cambridge: Cambridge University Press, 1913.

Heidel, Alexander. *The Babylonian Genesis*. Chicago: University of Chicago Press, 1942.

Hodges, Henry. *Technology in the Ancient World*. London: Allan Lane, 1970.

Jeans, James. *The Growth of Physical Science*, second edition. Cambridge: Cambridge University

Press, 1951.

Lucretius. *The Nature of the Universe*. New York: Penguin, 1951.

Murray, Gilbert. *Five Stages of Greek Religion*. New York: Anchor Books, 1952.

Russell, Bertrand. A *History of Western Philosophy*. New York: Simon and Schuster, 1945.

Sarton, George. A *History of Science*, Vols. 1 and 2. Cambridge: Harvard University Press, 1952,

1959.

Schrödinger, Erwin. *Nature and the Greeks*. Cambridge: Cambridge University Press, 1954.

Vlastos, Gregory. *Plato's Universe*. Seattle: University of Washington Press, 1975.

CHAPTER 8

Barnett, Lincoln. *The Universe and Dr. Einstein*. New York: Sloane, 1956.

Bernstein, Jeremy. *Einstein*. New York: Viking, 1973.

Borden, M. and Graham, O.L. *Speculations on American History*. Lexington, Mass.: D.C. Heath,

1977.

*Bussard, R.W. "Galactic Matter and Interstellar Flight." *Astronautica Acta*, Vol. 6, p. 179, 1960.

Cooper, Margaret. *The Inventions of Leonardo Da Vinci*. New York: Macmillan, 1965.

*Dole, S.H. "Formation of Planetary Systems by Aggregation: A Computer Simulation." *Icarus*,

Vol. 13, p. 494, 1970.

Dyson, F.J. "Death of a Project." [Orion.] *Science*, Vol. 149, p. 141, 1965.

Gamow, George. *Mr. Tompkins in Paperback*. Cambridge: Cambridge University Press, 1965.

Hart, Ivor B. *Mechanical Investigations of Leonardo Da Vinci*. Berkeley: University of California

Press, 1963.

Hoffman, Banesh. *Albert Einstein: Creator and Rebel*. New York: New American Library, 1972.

*Isaacman, R. and Sagan, Carl. "Computer Simulation of Planetary Accretion Dynamics:

Sensitivity to Initial Conditions."*Icarus*, Vol. 31, p. 510, 1977.

Lieber, Lillian R. and Lieber, Hugh Gray. *The Einstein Theory of Relativity*. New York: Holt,

Rinehart and Winston, 1961.

MacCurdy, Edward (ed.). *Notebooks of Leonardo*. Two volumes. New York: Reynal and

Hitchcock, 1938.

*Martin, A.R. (ed.). "Project Daedalus: Final Report of the

British Interplanetary Society Starship

Study." *Journal of the British Interplanetary Society*, Supplement, 1978.

McPhee, John A. *The Curve of Binding Energy*. New York: Farrar, Straus and Giroux, 1974.

*Mermin, David. *Space and Time and Special Relativity*. New York: McGraw-Hill, 1968.

Richter, Jean-Paul. *Notebooks of Leonardo Da Vinci*. New York: Dover, 1970.

Schlipp, Paul A. (ed.). *Albert Einstein: Philosopher-Scientist*, third edition. Two volumes. La Salle,

Ill: Open Court, 1970.

CHAPTER 9

Eddy, John A. *The New Sun: The Solar Results from Skylab*. NASA SP-402. Washington, D.C.: U.S.

Government Printing Office, 1979.

*Feynman, R.P., Leighton, R.B. and Sands, M. *The Feynman Lectures on Physics*. Reading, Mass.:

Addison-Wesley, 1963.

Gamow, George. *One, Two, Three ... Infinity*. New York:

Bantam Books, 1971.

Kasner, Edward and Newman, James R. *Mathematics and the Imagination.* New York: Simon and

Schuster, 1953.

Kaufmann, William J. *Stars and Nebulas.* San Francisco: W.H. Freeman, 1978.

Maffei, Paolo. *Monsters in the Sky.* Cambridge: M.I.T. Press, 1980.

Murdin, P. and Allen, D. *Catalogue of the Universe.* New York: Crown Publishers, 1979.

*Shklovskii, I.S. *Stars: Their Birth, Life and Death.* San Francisco: W.H. Freeman, 1978.

Sullivan, Walter. *Black Holes: The Edge of Space, The End of Time.* New York: Doubleday, 1979.

Weisskopf, Victor. *Knowledge and Wonder*, second edition. Cambridge: M.I.T. Press, 1979.

Excellent introductory college textbooks on astronomy include:

Abell, George. *The Realm of the Universe.* Philadelphia: Saunders College, 1980.

Berman, Louis and Evans, J.C. *Exploring the Cosmos.* Boston:

Little, Brown, 1980.

Hartmann, William K. *Astronomy: The Cosmic Journey*. Belmont, Cal.: Wadsworth, 1978.

Jastrow, Robert and Thompson, Malcolm H. *Astronomy: Fundamentals and Frontiers*, third

edition. New York: Wiley, 1977.

Pasachoff, Jay M. and Kutner, M.L. *University Astronomy*. Philadelphia: Saunders, 1978.

Zeilik, Michael. *Astronomy: The Evolving Universe*. New York: Harper and Row, 1979.

CHAPTER 10

Abbott, E. *Flatland*. New York: Barnes and Noble, 1963.

*Arp, Halton. "Peculiar Galaxies and Radio Sources." *Science*, Vol. 151, p. 1214, 1966.

Bok, Bart and Bok, Priscilla. *The Milky Way*, fourth edition. Cambridge: Harvard University

Press, 1974.

Campbell, Joseph. *The Mythic Image*. Princeton: Princeton University Press, 1974.

Ferris, Timothy. *Galaxies*. San Francisco: Sierra Club Books, 1980.

Ferris, Timothy. *The Red Limit: The Search by Astronomers for the Edge of the Universe*. New York:

William Morrow, 1977.

Gingerich, Owen (ed.). *Cosmology + 1*. A Scientific American Book. San Francisco: W.H.

Freeman, 1977.

*Jones, B. "The Origin of Galaxies: A Review of Recent Theoretical Developments and Their

Confrontation with Observation." *Reviews of Modern Physics*, Vol. 48, p. 107, 1976.

Kaufmann, William J. *Black Holes and Warped Space-Time*. San Francisco: W.H. Freeman, 1979.

Kaufmann, William J. *Galaxies and Quasars*. San Francisco: W.H. Freeman, 1979.

Rothenberg, Jerome (ed.). *Technicians of the Sacred*. New York: Doubleday, 1968.

Silk, Joseph, *The Big Bang: The Creation and Evolution of the Universe*. San Francisco: W.H.

Freeman, 1980.

Sproul, Barbara C. *Primal Myths: Creating the World.* New York: Harper and Row, 1979.

*Stockton, A.N. "The Nature of QSO Red Shifts." *Astrophysical Journal,* Vol. 223, p. 747, 1978.

Weinberg, Steven. *The First Three Minutes: A Modern View of the Origin of the Universe.* New York:

Basic Books, 1977.

*White, S.D.M. and Rees, M.J. "Core Condensation in Heavy Halos: A Two-Stage Series for

Galaxy Formation and Clustering." *Monthly Notices of the Royal Astronomical Society,* Vol. 183,

p. 341, 1978.

CHAPTER 11

Human Ancestors. Readings from Scientific American. San Francisco: W.H. Freeman, 1979.

Koestler, Arthur. *The Act of Creation.* New York: Macmillan, 1964.

Leakey, Richard E. and Lewin, Roger. *Origins.* New York: Dutton, 1977.

*Lehninger, Albert L. *Biochemistry*. New York: Worth Publishers, 1975.

*Norris, Kenneth S. (ed.). *Whales, Dolphins and Porpoises*. Berkeley: University of California Press,

1978.

*Payne, Roger and McVay, Scott. "Songs of Humpback Whales." *Science*, Vol. 173, p. 585,

August 1971.

Restam, Richard M. *The Brain*. New York: Doubleday, 1979.

Sagan, Carl. *The Dragons of Eden: Speculations on the Evolution of Human Intelligence*. New York:

Random House, 1977.

Sagan, Carl, Drake, F.D., Druyan, A., Ferris, T., Lomberg, J., and Sagan, L.S. *Murmurs of Earth:*

The Voyager Interstellar Record. New York: Random House, 1978.

*Stryer, Lubert. *Biochemistry*. San Francisco: W.H. Freeman, 1975.

The Brain. A Scientific American Book. San Francisco: W.H. Freeman, 1979.

*Winn, Howard E. and Olla, Bori L. (eds.). *Behavior of Marine Animals*, Vol. 3: *Cetaceans*. New

York: Plenum, 1979.

CHAPTER 12

Asimov, Isaac. *Extraterrestrial Civilizations*. New York: Fawcett, 1979.

Budge, E.A. Wallis. *Egyptian Language: Easy Lessons in Egyptian Hieroglyphics*. New York: Dover

Publications, 1976.

de Laguna, Frederica. *Under Mount St. Elias: History and Culture of Yacutat Tlingit*. Washington,

D.C.: U.S. Government Printing Office, 1972.

Emmons, G.T. *The Chilkat Blanket*. New York: Memoirs of the American Museum of Natural

History, 1907.

Goldsmith, D. and Owen, T. *The Search for Life in the Universe*. Menlo Park: Benjamin/Cummings,

1980.

Klass, Philip. *UFO's Explained*. New York: Vintage, 1976.

Krause, Aurel. *The Tlingit Indians.* Seattle: University of Washington Press, 1956.

La Pérouse, Jean F. de G., comte de. *Voyage de la Pérouse Autour du Monde* (four volumes). Paris:

Imprimerie de la Republique, 1797.

Mallove, E., Forward, R.L., Paprotny, Z., and Lehmann, J. "Interstellar Travel and

Communication: A Bibliography." *Journal of the British Interplanetary Society*, Vol. 33, No. 6,

1980.

*Morrison, P., Billingham, J. and Wolfe, J. (eds.). *The Search for Extraterrestrial Intelligence.* New

York: Dover, 1979.

*Sagan, Carl (ed.). *Communication with Extraterrestrial Intelligence (CETI).* Cambridge: M.I.T.

Press, 1973.

Sagan, Carl and Page, Thornton (eds.). *UFO's: A Scientific Debate.* NewYork: W.W. Norton, 1974.

Shklovskii, I.S. and Sagan, Carl. *Intelligent Life in the Universe.* New York: Dell, 1967.

Story, Ron. *The Space-Gods Revealed: A Close Look at the Theories of Erich von Daniken*. New York:

Harper and Row, 1976.

Vaillant, George C. *Aztecs of Mexico*. New York: Pelican Books, 1965.

CHAPTER 13

Drell, Sidney D. and Von Hippel, Frank. "Limited Nuclear War." *Scientific American*, Vol. 235, p.

2737, 1976.

Dyson, F. *Disturbing the Universe*. New York: Harper and Row, 1979.

Glasstone, Samuel (ed.). *The Effects of Nuclear Weapons*. Washington, D.C.: U.S. Atomic Energy

Commission, 1964.

Humboldt, Alexander von. *Cosmos*. Five volumes. London: Bell, 1871.

Murchee, G. *The Seven Mysteries of Life*. Boston: Houghton Mifflin, 1978.

Nathan, Otto and Norden, Heinz (eds.). *Einstein on Peace*. New York: Simon and Schuster, 1960.

Perrin, Noel. *Giving Up the Gun: Japan's Reversion to the Sword 1543–1879*. Boston: David Godine,

1979.

Prescott, James W. "Body Pleasure and the Origins of Violence." *Bulletin of the Atomic Scientists*,

p. 10, November 1975.

*Richardson, Lewis F. *The Statistics of Deadly Quarrels*. Pittsburgh: Boxwood Press, 1960.

Sagan, Carl. *The Cosmic Connection. An Extraterrestrial Perspective*. New York: Doubleday, 1973.

World Armaments and Disarmament. SIPRI Yearbook, 1980 and previous years, Stockholm

International Peace Research Institute. New York: Crane Russak and Company, 1980 and

previous years.

APPENDICES

Courant, Richard and Robbins, Herbert. *What Is Mathematics? An Elementary Approach to Ideas*

and Methods. New York: Oxford University Press, 1969.

Conclusion

Questions that are yet to be answered, theories that are yet to be proven, when will we humans cherish life and value it? The thing that we needed the most, our home, is slowly being destroyed by us. We humans are naturally hostile because of our reptilian brain, but our mammalian brain and intelligence enable us to be more humane compared to other lifeforms. With every action comes a conclusion. This conclusion should be positive in order to create and maintain harmonious relationships of every race in this world. As well as for other lifeforms in the future.

Fascinations with the depth of the cosmic ocean are partnered with curiosity. Communicating with other lifeforms is a daunting task at present, it will require many more years to discover other lifeforms in the cosmos. We can only hope that our race, our civilization will survive long enough to acquire more knowledge, wisdom, and to have more discoveries in the distant future regarding our ever expanding universe.

In chapter 1, we have learned that the cosmos is so vast that we can consider ourselves as feeble creations of it. Our world is nothing but a shore with the vast cosmic ocean surrounding it.

In chapter 2, we wondered if there are other lifeforms in the cosmic ocean. What are the chances of finding one? Even if it is slim, we still have to try.

In chapter 3, we have learned that the cosmos, helped people to unite and brings harmony to our civilization through common interests and goals.

In chapter 4, we have learned that the Earth is our mother, willing to punish us for our misdeeds. Earth gives us life, but it can also claim our life through disasters. The cosmos can choose to destroy our civilization through phenomena such as meteor strikes. But the Earth will still help us survive, so care for our home and mother.

In chapter 5, we explore Mars, and how humans have explored the gentle red planet. Lifeforms in Mars is not plausible but still, we humans could opt to live in Mars one day.

Chapter 6, the tales of the travelers. With epic voyages are epic tales as well. May it be here on our Earth or in space. Especially towards the planet Jupiter, different explorations have been done to increase our understanding of the gentle giant.

Chapter 7, the night sky is full of stars. These stars are the backbone of the night. These stars might have their own planets surrounding them may it be dead or inhabitable. One day, we will find lifeforms in the planets surrounding these stars.

Chapter 8, the travels in space and time. Travelling into space is a difficult task, requiring an enormous amount of resources. One day however, we will extend our reach towards other galaxies in the vast cosmos.

Chapter 9, we have learned that stars have a life cycle. They all die one day just like us humans. Millions of years from now, our sun will die. Cherish every single second of light that our sun is giving to us, because one day, the very light that gives us life will be the cause of our extinction.

Chapter 10, the edge of forever. The universe is still expanding until now, not just in a constant pace, but in an accelerating pace, growing bigger and bigger.

Chapter 11, all information gathered by mankind, one day will be stored and replicated. Just like the DNA, storing and replicating blueprints of species.

Chapter 12, hopefully, one day, we humans will be part of some intergalactic federation. Like a federation of galactic citizens. Being part of the bigger picture, which is still a small piece in the cosmic puzzle.

Chapter 13, the last chapter. We humans speaks for Earth, we humans also threaten Earth. Cherishing everything and caring for our civilization will ensure humanity's survival for thousands of years to come. We need to unite for a greater cause, for the cosmos.

Proof of a living God is still being discovered, but proofs of the cosmos, the place where we came from, are everywhere. Surround yourself with the cosmos, be curious, be smart. We are its greatest creation so fat after all.

Final Thoughts

Hey! Did you enjoy this book? We sincerely hope you thoroughly enjoyed this short read and have gotten immensely valuable insights that will help you in any areas of your life.

Would it be too greedy if we ask for a review from you?

It takes 1 minute to leave 1 review to possibly influence 1 more person's decision to read just 1 book which may change their 1 life. Your 1 minute matters and we value it and thank you so much for giving us your 1 minute. If it sucks, just say it sucks. Period.

FREE BONUS

P.S. Is it okay if we overdeliver?

Here at Abbey Beathan Publishing, we believe in overdelivering way beyond our reader's expectations. Is it okay if we overdeliver?

Here's the deal, we're going to give you an extremely valuable cheatsheet of "Accelerated Learning". We've partnered up with Ikigai Publishing to present to you the exclusive bonus of "Accelerated Learning Cheatsheet"

What's the catch? We need to trust you… You see, we want to overdeliver and in order for us to do that, we've to trust our reader to keep this bonus a secret to themselves. Why? Because we don't want people to be getting our exclusive accelerated learning cheatsheet without even buying our books itself. Unethical, right?

Ok. Are you ready?

Simply Visit this link: http://bit.ly/acceleratedcheatsheet

We hope you'll enjoy our free bonuses as much as we've enjoyed preparing it for you!

Free Bonus #2: Free Book Preview of Summary: Dreams from my Father

The Book at a Glance

Chapter 1 is all about Barack Obama's origins. He was born to a white mother and a black African father. His grandparents were witness to racial discrimination in the past, and their being liberal-minded and how they respected "colored" people led to his parents union. Although Barack's father left them when he was only 2 years old, his mother and grandparents never spoke ill of him. They still remembered and shared their memories of him as a dignified, intelligent, and graceful gentleman.

Chapter 2 talks about how Barack immigrated to Indonesia when his mother married an Indonesian. In the new country, he turned to his stepfather Lolo for guidance and advice. He learned how to survive, and learned life-long values such as honesty, fairness, and being straightforward. He was also exposed to the cruel world of poverty and violence.

Chapter 3 brings him back to America, where he was required to go to school. His mother stayed in Indonesia with Lolo and his new sister, Maya. She would later join him in America. He would also meet his father for the first time since he left. He would live with him for a month and get to know the father that he never knew.

Chapter 4 shares how Barack went through high school and his experiences living with his grandparents. In fact, he had an eye-opening experience when his grandmother was harassed by a black man on the way to work. As a result, he turned to books trying to search for answers to his identity and on the roots of racism.

In chapter 5, Barack, having found his voice, became active in school rallies. During this time, his mother talked him into building a future by starting college. He would turn to one of his gramps' friends, Frank the poet, and would be warned to keep his eyes open. It was a difficult time, and he further experienced an identity crisis.

In chapter 6, Barack takes the opportunity of a transfer program to Columbia University and transfers to Manhattan. He stays with a Pakistani friend who was an illegal immigrant and became serious about his studies. During the summer, when his mother visited him with Maya, his sister, he would learn of the true story behind his parents' separation and would serve as a realization. He would carry his father's memories even after his death and find a new identity for himself in light of his father.

Chapter 7 talks about how Barack was inspired to become an organizer. He was promoted as a financial writer but later resigned his post. At first, his dreams of becoming an organizer slipped away, if not for his half-sister's phone call that gave him a push. He got hired by a Jewish organizer, Marty Kaufman, and set off to Chicago.

Chapter 8 shows Barack's first few days as an organizer in Chicago. He attended the CCRC rally, which composed of people who were laid off from work. The first few days were full of challenges as there was trouble talking to people and coming up with an issue that everyone believed was worth fighting for.

In chapter 10, Barack was almost ready to give up. However, his and his co-organizers realizations motivated him to do better and make a difference. In the end, he was successful in organizing a meeting with the Mayor's Office Employment and Training (MET), and the result was a promise to have a MET intake center within the vicinity in six months' time.

Chapter 10 speaks of winter, which was a time of realization for Barack. From the stories he heard from the organization leaders, he realized that they were fighting for a cause due to their past – just like him. This led him to open up and relate better to others.

Barack finally meets his half-sister from Kenya, named Auma, in chapter 11. During her visit, she told him things about their father, which made him get to know him from another's point of view. It was in this reunion with her sister that he finally felt free from the memories of his father.

Chapter 12 talks about the success Barack was finally making as an organizer. He eventually separated ways with this boss, Marty. They were able to launch the new MET intake center in Roseland, and also get some young parents involved in fighting for health causes.

In chapter 13, Barack employed a recruit named Johnnie, whom he got along well. He also visited his half-brother in Washington, D.C., and learned more from him. However, Roy's attitude towards their father was more of bitterness.

Chapter 14 talks about how Barack decided to pursue law at Harvard and selected Johnnie to replace him as lead organizer. Their current project was to target the public schools with the help of religious congregations. Barack attended his first ever service and was moved to tears with the realization of hope.

Chapter 15 brings Barack to Kenya, where he meets British men on the plane who were to make up for the "lack of trained professionals" in Kenya. He managed to have his luggage accidentally sent to Johannesburg, and was helped by a lovely stewardess who knew his father. He felt a sense of belonging in Kenya, but the locals still saw him as American.

In chapter 16, Barack meets his other relatives and learns of the rift among his two aunts, Zeituni and Sarah, due to his father's inheritance. He also meets with his half-brother, seventeen-year-old Bernard. Later on, he would meet his father's other wife, Ruth, and his stepbrother Mark, who also studies in America.

Chapter 17 is a family reunion, when Roy comes home to Kenya earlier than expected. Barack and Auma had just come back from a safari, and he was enjoying the last few days of his vacation.

Chapter 18 introduces more of Barack's extended family. He met his grandmother, two uncles, and his grandfather's brother. He also noticed that people would always ask him for something when he arrived. His relatives highly regarded him due to his father's stories about him.

In chapter 19, Barack learns more about his grandfather's discipline and how he prospered due to hard work, about his father's diligence to study abroad, and about the events that happened to his father. He finally understood and felt complete.

The epilogue fast-forwards to the future. Barack pursued law and gave back to the community by helping out community organizers and churches. He met his future wife, Michelle, who was immediately loved by his family. They got married despite some deaths in both their families.

Part 1: Origins

Chapter 1

Barack Obama was named after his father, who was an African Kenyan and a member of the Luo tribe. His father was a smart man who won a scholarship in Nairobi and was among the chosen few who attended university in the United States. He was the first African student at the University of Hawaii, where he graduated at the top of his class, and became president of the International Students Association. He also met his future wife in Hawaii. However, he was asked to go back to Africa for his duties. His son, Barack or Barry, was only two years old at that time. Mother and son remained in the United States.

Barack Junior's mother and grandparents talked fondly of his father. His grandparents told him of a story wherein a white man at the bar was being racist and tried to humiliate his father. His father lectured the man. As a result, the man tried to buy his forgiveness. When Barack was 21, his aunt Jane, who had been a stranger until then, called from Nairobi. She announced that his father had died in a car crash.

One of the things that Barack wondered about was why his mother's parents permitted her to marry his father. Barack's mother was white, and his father was African and black. Eventually, he learned that his grandparents were raised in decent and respectable families, so discrimination was not known. His grandparents also told stories about their past, which were filled with romance, drama, and action. In fact, the stories were always interesting. He also learned that his grandparents eloped just before the Pearl Harbor bombing and that his grandfather enlisted in the army.

His grandfather was also the adventurous type who loved to venture on new starts. He was also poetic and a freethinker. This liberal-mindedness paved the way for his father's invitation to dinner. When Barack's mother invited his father for dinner, his grandfather was struck by his resemblance to his favorite singer, Nat King Cole. When dinner ended, his grandparents commented how dignified, intelligent, and graceful he was – and he also loved his British accent.

When the family moved to Texas, they had their experiences with racial discrimination. These incidents explained why his grandparents allowed his white mother to marry a black man. First was when his grandmother, called Toot or Tutu, spoke with a World War II veteran who was black. She addressed him as Mr. Reed and found him to be very dignified. However, she was called out by the secretary that black men should never be addressed as "Mister". She continued calling him Mr. Reed, but the janitor kept his distance.

Another instance was when his mother came home one day from school and befriended a black girl. The other students threw stones at them and called his mother a "nigger lover". The next day, Barack's grandfather took a leave from work, spoke to the principal, and reported the students who had thrown stones. The principal responded that white girls should not play with colored races.

Eventually, Barack's mother and father were married by a justice of the peace in a quiet ceremony; then, they moved to Hawaii. In Hawaii, there were many different cultures such as Japanese, Chinese, and Filipino. Racism was a thing of the past in Hawaii, and here is where the family became comfortable.

However, Barack still wondered why his father left. His mother and grandparents painted a picture of how amazing he was, but he still did not understand. He even found articles about his father and a photograph of him. Barack felt that something was amiss in his childhood and he grew older, not knowing his father.